WAKE UP, STUPID

WAKE UP, STUPID

by **MARK HARRIS**, 1922-

New York 1959

ALFRED A. KNOPF

L. C. Catalog card number: 59–9225

THIS IS A BORZOI BOOK,
PUBLISHED BY ALFRED A. KNOPF, INC.

Published July 20, 1959
Second Printing, August 1959

Acknowledgment is made to United Press International for permission to reprint their dispatch appearing on page 31, and to Pilgrim Tract Society Incorporated of Randleman, North Carolina, publisher of the tracts appearing on pages 24 and 139.

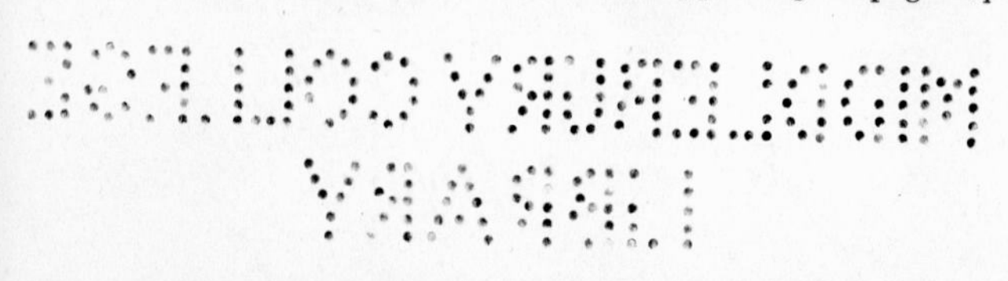

FOR

MARTHA AND HENRY

AND THEIR MOTHER AND FATHER

WAKE UP, STUPID

Monday, October 1

[*to Abner Klang, New York*]

October 1

Dear Abner,

This morning I sent off to you air-mail a four-pound play in one marathon act, which I call *Boswell's Manhattan Journal.* Notify me of its arrival.

I hope it doesn't bore you, although I don't in the least demand nor expect that you will read it. I hope, too, that you will contrive to gather yourself together long enough to behave toward it in an appropriate manner. Since it is—I remind you—a play, there is no point in submitting it to *Reader's Digest* or *Ring* magazine or *The Year's Best Cross-word Puzzles* or *Zip* or *Collier's.* Try to discard your absurd notions of where "the top" is. You might try, first, the man who produced Paul Purdy's play, and who is now doing *Sweet Girl.* I forget his name. What's his name?

After you have done something more or less reasonable, go have your typewriter fixed, you phool, and then telephone Mr. Wenk and tell him not to communicate with me further. He sent me his script, which I glanced at, which appeared to me to be as crude and incomprehensible as he himself, and which I thereupon returned to him. I am divorced from that project, and you may tell him so, though God knows I hate to put two ideas into your head at once.

I have here a series of letters and telegrams from you, dating back as far as April 22, which I have not answered because, as you may now see for yourself, I have been heroically at work. You may always know that when I do not reply to your mail I am at work or dead, preferably the former.

Let me anticipate your immediate question by replying No, I am at work on nothing else at the moment, and I have no plans except to romance my wife, amuse my children, lie on the back of my neck, hold down my job, and consort with select friends until my energies are restored. I worked thirteen months on the play, with scarcely a night's interruption.

Good luck,

Tuesday, October 2

[to Harold Rosenblatt, New Haven, Conn.]

October 2

Dear Harold,

Yesterday I sent off to you a carbon copy of the play, which I completed Friday morning at four o'clock, after which I went to bed and slept halfway into Saturday. I woke up hungry. Paul and Willa and Red and Rosemary came in the evening but left early in deference either to Willa's pregnancy or my post-partum exhaustion, although not until after we lamented at length your absence. Paul will produce the play at University Theater, beginning probably after Christmas.

Now I am faced with the task of fulfilling all vows made while the work-in-progress was in progress. I am going to catch up on my mail, an insane resolve which, in the past, far from relieving me of entanglements, has only drawn me into new confusion, controversy, and conflict. Fortunately I am wiser now than in the past.

I am also going to inquire into routes of escape from this wretched profession. Toward this end a sad beginning was attempted yesterday morning as I stood in front of the post-office at 18th & Diamond, my manuscript gone off to the other end of the continent, the American flag waving in the breeze above, and I with empty hands and nowhere to go. I had declared a holiday. Said I, "I shall go whither I am drawn," and I was drawn to school, so that my holiday seems to have lasted only a minute or so.

Madly shall I cultivate my Tenure. Madly shall I assume administrative responsibilities. Yesterday I smilingly assumed, *pro tem* in your selfish absence, chairmanship of The Committee on Freshman Staff, which Mr. Gamble offered. He did not fail, first, however, to observe that I have been denied the privilege of committee service, the result, as he speculated, of my rather irregular attendance (or, to use his quaint terminology, my "rather regular absence") at general staff meetings.

I do not, in any case, expect to hold Mr. Gamble, and probably not Harbidge, but I do depend upon Paul, and Paul's influence over the cowardly Clinch. This, coupled with support I hope to enlist from Mr. Outerbridge, should give me at the critical instant the necessary majority, to wit:

Definitely For Me	*Definitely Against Me*
Paul Purdy	Mr. Gamble
Clinch (cowed by Paul)	Harbidge
Mr. Outerbridge	

I have your note of the 16th, and Beth and I are pleased that you are settled in. Did I tell you of my Harvard offer? Of course I shall not go, but it is a mouse with which to tease the local cats: dare Mr. Gamble let me be dropped if it be known that Harvard wants me? Beth and I agree that the chief advantage—indeed, the sole and single advantage of the possibility—is Harvard's proximity to the Boswell papers at Yale.

Now, tell me what you think of the following proposition, which arises from my present indolence. I propose that you and I keep a Journal, mailing, say once a week, our entries to each other. Pending your reply, I am vowed to write each night at least one useful letter to a friend or enemy. I must write a little something every night, as a fighter punches the bag a little every day. It may be that in the end my fame shall rest upon my letters, or our Journal, and it will be seen that, although I was surely a fool, I had desirable friends and nasty enemies, and I always wrote a crafty prose. These letters, or our Journal, will be the history of the way a certain kind of man lived his life in a certain year in a certain age on a certain planet.

Dots-and-dashes-and-lots-of-flashes-from-border-to-border-and-coast-to-coast: Peggy Chambliss and Oliver Thompson are become illegal man and wife . . . Clinch has written his 14,547th quatrain commemorating the villainy of his father . . . Red Traphagen says the reason for their September failure was angry gods and bad pitching . . . George Cofax grew a mustache over his lip over the summer . . . *The Foghorn* will henceforth be published twice a week . . . I have been very nearly excommunicated from the Church . . . the beat generation is bleeding all over North Beach . . . I am going to murder Cecile.

Love and kisses,

Wednesday, October 3

[to Clinton W. Blalock, Harvard University]

October 3

Dear Blalock:

Once upon a time you expressed the thought that Harvard might want me if I wanted it, or her, or him, or them. Tell me now what you think.

You know, I long for the variety of seasons, which we do not have here. This city offers no nostalgia, and a writer cannot live without nostalgia. I am nostalgic for nostalgia.

I have just finished my Boswell-Johnson play, upon which I labored for many months. It has been, for me, the major effort of my life, and I have hoped, as I have written it, that it might satisfy the demands of the best taste, such as yours. Perhaps, if we are all lucky, we will have the opportunity to see it somewhere played.

If you should get over to Yale, look up my friend Harold Rosenblatt, on a year's leave there. You will find him up to his hips in the Boswell papers.

My best wishes to you,

Thursday, October 4

[to Whizzer Harlow, Santa Fé, New Mexico]

October 4

Dear Whizzer,

Are you there? I have your several letters from remote points of the globe. It is too bad I am not a stamp-collector. I was wondering what you were doing all of a sudden in Hawaii, and now you make me wonder what you are doing in New Mexico, where I am glad I am not at. "Having," as Boswell said, "no exquisite relish of the beauties of Nature . . . being more delighted with the busy hum of men," I prefer it here, where Nature leaves a man at peace with the illusion that he is large. I have finished my play, I am schoolmastering again, and I am sitting around thinking up mischief.

I acknowledge receipt of the key, and I have no objection to performing the errand, but I am wondering if it might wait until after I have stood my trial for Tenure here. You will say that I am a moral coward.

Anyhow (by way of easing into braver word of myself), Tom Katt asked me some time ago if I'd care to jump, and I said I would, as soon as I finished my play, whereupon, last Saturday, he and I and Earl went aloft. The plan was for me to jump, and Tom and Earl to meet me below.

Earl wanted to jump, too, but his mother expressly forbade it.

But now—on and up into the realms of pure telepathy—I must tell you that, as we climbed, Earl insisted upon jumping, refused to stay in the plane with Tom, and this I could not deny him, however Beth might rage; and so, together, his arms about my neck, we leapt, and Earl said, "The family that leaps together keeps together," and we fell and opened and drifted.

Earl said, "Now we are ready for Lesson Two. What do we do when we hit?"

"Just stay loose," I said, "and keep your knees wiggly." He was confident because I told him he was confident. It is how my father raised me. A man can do anything his father tells him he can do. My father always told me (killing time here, while Earl and I are drifting) I could be, if not Heavyweight Champion of the World, the world's most courageous liar. Once we received a visit from the Salt-Lake Youngdahls whom, because of my father's antipathy to them, I also hated; when they arrived I informed them that I had lately become blind, and I walked about the house with my arms outstretched, shuffling my feet, asking each speaker to "identify himself" until my ears should compensate my loss of vision. I regularly insisted upon people's telling me the time, enumerating the contents of dishes set before me, reading aloud to me; all this quite enraged the Salt-Lake folk, and the visit deteriorated into an argument between them and my father as to whether it was not over-indulging a child to allow him to play at tragedy. "God," said my Uncle Hock, chief of the Salt-Lake clan, "gave him sight." "God gave him also," my father argued, "the power to imagine otherwise," and so they all disputed while my brother and my cousins, so persuasively blind I was, led me about by the arm, told me the weather, and wondered how I should earn my living.

It is one of the large moments of my life—drifting, I mean, with Earl, his arms about my neck, and he held tight and stayed loose, and we hit and rolled and laughed, and Tom hit, too, hit something, I don't know what it was nor how it happened, but he couldn't stay up, and there was bound to be Tom's day—wasn't there?—and the crash was loud, and a brief, bright flame, but loud enough and bright enough to have made Tom proud, and which he might even have admired, even then, in the final moments of his final Saturday.

Sadly,

Friday, October 5

[to his mother, Ogden, Utah]

October 5

Dear Mom,

I'm in a state of nervous prostration as a result of finishing my play, and now school is upon us again, but I take this evening to acknowledge your several letters, as well as to add to Beth's note to you my appreciation for the lovely gift for Tetsey's birthday.

Mainly I want to clarify the matter of Bishop Veenstra's visit. I did not—and how the phrase has come into existence I am perplexed to know—"throw him out of the house." Although he interrupted me at my labors, I was as cordial as ever a man could have been under the circumstances. We served him tea, and we inquired the state of the domestic Church and its missions overseas, whereupon he itemized for us, by no means hurriedly, the number of converts baptized this year, nation by nation in Europe, and bath-house by bath-house throughout heathen Asia.

He informed me that my excommunication is far from final. I might, if I wish, protest the action and apply for suspension of so harsh a punishment to the proper authorities in Salt Lake. I told him, however, that I accept gracefully my punishment, that I have done the Church no good in all my years, that the devil is in me, and that the best love I can demonstrate is to allow myself, in the interest of the Church's reputation, to be dropped without fuss.

This issue being soon and clearly defined, an impasse was acknowledged, regret was expressed upon all sides, and he departed. The discussion was entirely amiable.

You ask me if I wrote the TV play. No. It is scheduled for the 26th, New-York time. It is to be, as the TV people say, "live," although the adaptor, who was here for a week and asked the same silly questions every day, appeared to me quite dead. As for the Ogden papers, you may give them material from the book-jackets, or you may speak to them from memory, for you know even better than I my dates. I'm sorry I can't oblige with a recent photograph, but I have none.

Tell Dad and Dee they may see Garafolo's new fighter on TV on the 12th.

Harold and Sylvia are settled at Yale for the year. I am jealous. The Purdys are expecting again. Red is back from the baseball wars. Whizzer Harlow is living in New Mexico, and the Outerbridges are coming to dinner tomorrow night.

We'll be home for Thanksgiving. Until then,

Much much love,

P.S. Maybe Dad would care to drop a friendly little note to Mr. Outerbridge, whom I see almost every day and who never fails to ask for you-all. Just address him @ the English Department.

Saturday, October 6

[to Louis Garafolo, McLaren's Camp,
Scottsdale, Arizona]

October 6

My ever dear Garafolo,

Please pardon my unpardonable delay in answering your letter, but I hasten now to fire off a letter to you before you break camp. Of *course* I will want to see you if and when you pass through. Can the day ever come that I won't want to see you? No, no, no, a thousand times no.

I am back at the old stand because I didn't have the courage to quit, and if I quit I wouldn't know what to do with myself. God knows I love the sight of the check every month, which leaves me free to rest between the big fights, save myself for the main events, not have to fight for bread.

How is the weather on your bones down there? Good luck on the 12th. I am sure Irwin is everything you say he is, because you wouldn't say so if he weren't. Needless to say I hope so, and I will do my part at this end with prayer.

Always and always your boy,

Sunday, October 7

[*from Abner Klang, New York, special delivery*]

October 5 Lee you are a genius. Who but you would ever dream o making a play out o the li e o Olsen and Johnson much less do it. I oresee or this play a nice little prestige run o maybe a hundred nights similar to Paul Purdy which I am sad to say shuts down this week netting you about $1000 a week and giving you a chance o slamming down the lid on your desk at the college and keeping your nose exclusively to the writing grindstone. What are you working on now.

Your interest only at heart I started at the top with my intimate riend Bartholomew Enright with two shows now running on Broadway and told him I want a ast reading. Producer of Bonanza Boat and The amily Place. Naturally I will keep you abreast o everything as usual. I am keeping in touch with him night and day in said regard.

On to other matters I sent to your bank $3000 less agency commission representing TV payment or the Hard Puncher. I can't see why you can't see your way clear to giving them a little co-operation over at Window 9. A suggestion. Also $1480 less agency commission covering miscellaneous royalties and reprints. Make sure your bank puts it in.

By the way Colliers olded some time ago.

Answering your question the name o Purdy's producer is T. T. Tattershall who I would never show your play i he was the only remaining man on earth except as a last resort. It is my experience he took three years getting Sweet Girl in production. He will sit on an option without action complaining that he can never ind the right directors or actors. Why he does this is a total mystery with talent lining the streets.

I Enright or as soon as any other producer grabs this up I am going to include in your contract a trip to New York all expenses and you and I will parade around a little bit on the streets where ladies live.

Whizzer Harlow is in Arizona but why he doesn't stay still in one place is beyond my understanding. A man cannot write with one leg in the street in my humble opinion. Congratulations to you and Purdy got rid of the ants in your respective pants. Tell Traphagen to dash out a book or better still why don't you ghost it or him. It is the national game and a steady picture market.

A business man is kissing his wi e goodby at Penn Station on his way to close a big Miami deal and sees over her shoulder a gal kissing her husband goodby. Needless to say she is beauti ul. On the train the man and the gal all into conversation. They have a drink together. They have supper together. She is also going to Miami. They discover that their roomettes or whatever you call them because I haven't been on a train in years are right next door. So the irst thing anybody knows they are between the sheets together and when he is done he sits up and begins to cry. She says why are you crying and he says he is crying because I never be ore engaged in extra marital delectation and am thinking about my beauti ul wi e and three children back home in New Rochelle orty ive minutes rom Broadway. She also begins to

[*here the fragment ends*]

105 Yukon Street
San Francisco 14
October 7

Mr. Harry Searle
Larkspur, California

Dear Mr. Searle:

I am sorry not to have replied sooner to your letter of February 19 containing your kind invitation to me to join The Dollar A Word Club, and sending me, also, an application blank. Actually, I have never earned at the rate of a dollar a word, although my mother, for a concluding line in a jingle contest, once won a Kaiser automobile.

Even if I were eligible to join, however, some of my friends tell me that The Dollar A Word Club should, for the sake of correctness, hyphenate itself: a compound adjective *is,* after all, a compound adjective.

Nevertheless, the honor of a letter from you is not to be taken lightly, and I should not at all object to hearing from you again, your time permitting.

Fraternally,
Lee W. Youngdahl

Monday, October 8

[*from Victor Wenk*]

WINDOW 9
Rockefeller Center
New York 20

October 5

Dear Lee—

Your agent tells me how busy you are—and I do not want to interupt you—as I know how it is—but if you can spare a minute please answer only one point for convenience's sake—in my letter to you—the point referred to being the speech the referee makes to the two fighters—at the begining of the fight.

Everybody agrees the play is coming along greatly—and everyone concerned are pleased with the progress being made—it is going to be a great hit. I am speaking to your agent about doing the screenplay—which I am sure will folo—as every show done on Window 9 has been bought—in the past.

I know how busy you are—as he tells me—so I will only send along best wishes to you—in your fair city—I wish I lived there—far from the madening crowd.

Gabriella Bodeen quit the cast—just as well—

she is too big for the part—in body as well as in temperament.

Gratefully,

[to Abner Klang, New York, special delivery]

October 8

Dear Abner,

For everybody else the World Series may be over, but for you, my dear fellow, it is the ninth inning of the seventh game, and somebody has hit you a long fly ball, and you had better go and get it: I have here an idiotic letter from Wenk, which reminds me to remind you to review once again with the people at Window 9 the matter of billing. Crack of the bat! Start running!

Since they persist in their desire to retain the title they must, as agreed, proceed according to my plan. I have not had confirmation from you of their agreement.

The title, *The Hard Puncher,* may appear only:

1. In isolation, or,
2. In isolated juxtaposition to my name.

In short, Mr. Wenk's name is to appear:

1. Nowhere in juxtaposition to the title, and,
2. Nowhere in juxtaposition to my name.

Mr. Wenk's name may appear:

1. *Only* in isolation, attached to the phrase, "a television adaptation by . . ."

The following would be ideal:

One flash: The Hard Puncher, based upon the Lee-Youngdahl novel.

Separate flash: a television adaptation by Victor Wenk.

This should be as clear as the white ball against the blue sky. Run hard, and never mind the fences, because if you here fail to preserve me from mortification in the eyes of the world you will have all the winters of your life to rest up, and I shall be off playing ball with fleeter agents. Dig!

Wrathfully,

October 8

Mr. Victor Wenk
@ Window 9
Rockefeller Center
New York 20
New York

Dear Mr. Wenk:
Eliminate the speech.

Yours truly,

ENCLOSURE

Lee W. Youngdahl
105 Yukon Street
San Francisco 14
California

[*enclosure to Victor Wenk*]

TV AND THE CHRISTIAN

WASTED MONEY SPIRITUAL NEGLECT WASTED TIME

TELEVISION is the greatest menace of modern times, and how Christians are going to be able to make use of it I don't know. Anyone who has seen it must be convinced of its danger. It has been proven that the eye-gate appeal makes a much greater appeal than the ear-gate, and while there are good programs on television there are so many of the other kind that it is going to be most difficult to put on one and blot out the other.

I am shocked when I visit homes where television is installed. No sooner are the parents out of the room than the children, boys and girls in their teens and younger still, hurry to the television set, stretched on the floor, and what are they looking at? A bloody wrestling match where two men are tearing each other to pieces, trying to gouge out each other's eyes! And as the children watch and listen to the groans and cries of the wrestlers they can hardly control themselves. A night club show, women for the most part unclad, drinking and smoking, going through sensual dances, every action plainly visible, the entire scene revolting and demoralizing. Now boxing bouts are brought into the home and displayed before our very children's eyes, the scene fascinates them.

(Ed. note. Not only are the Baptist guilty, but many thousands of professed Christians in other Churches.)

A polluted diet of crime, violence, brutality, and sadism sponsored by cigarette companies, breweries and distillers, is now the daily menu for millions of boys and girls. The Theater, with all its filth, that we as Christians wouldn't dream of patronizing, is now brought into our living rooms. Television may well be the final step in the complete collapse of our moral and spiritual life in the nation. Children will do what they see others doing.

Children have been known to use knives on their parents when they insisted on turning it off. Alcoholism has almost doubled since television began to feature liquor ads. If you want to know how serious it is, read the article on page 103 of the Reader's Digest for April, 1956. Robbery with violence is increasing by leaps and bounds. What kind of a harvest can we expect?

(Ed. note. Few have been able to control TV in their homes.)

I predict that if ever a real Holy Ghost, Heaven-born revival comes to Grand Rapids or any other city, one of the first thing folks will do, without the preacher's prompting, is to get rid of that cesspool of iniquity called TV. "Then came Isaiah the prophet unto King Hezekiah, and said unto him, what said these men? and from whence came they unto thee? And Hezekiah said, They are come from a far country, even from Babylon. And he said, "What have they SEEN IN THINE HOUSE?" *II Kings 20:14-15.*

(PILGRIM TRACT SOCIETY, *Randleman, N. C.* Supported by voluntary gifts of its readers. Tracts free as the Lord supplies the funds. Send postage for 100 samples of tracts.)

Tuesday, October 9

[to Harold Rosenblatt, New Haven, Conn.]

October 9

Dear Harold,

Hello hello. Hello hello hello. Nobody home. But somebody *must* be home. In particular, I am eager to know whether my play has reached you, and my letter of a week ago. After I mail off a manuscript I watch to see what planes go down, but, since none fell, I assume the arrival of my play to your hand. I trust you to catch me in errors or anachronisms, although, speaking modestly, I expect there are few: as Boswell ran half over London to check the smallest fact, so did I run half over the libraries of the Bay Area in the same cause. To combine, as I think I did in the play, the logic of scholarship with the logic of imagination, is surely, as you must agree, no small feat. You had best agree: if you don't you are wrong.

A week of school gone by. Only eight months to summer. The Outerbridges were here for dinner Saturday night and asked for you, he most congenial, but I a little uneasy that he did not laugh harder at the tale of my excommunication. Although my religious beliefs, as I took care to remark, have been somewhat shaped by *Job: A Disquisition,* he took this as less than a compliment, and renounced his work as the labor of a young fool. The Purdys and the Traphagens also were present, and they afterward expressed the feeling that Outerbridge likes me well enough, or, in any case, must support me out of ancient regional alliance, wherefore the universe now orders itself thus:

Definitely For Me	*Definitely Against Me*
Paul Purdy	Mr. Gamble
Clinch (satellite to Paul)	Harbidge
Mr. Outerbridge	

You tell me nothing of my idea for an exchange of Journals with you. You tell me nothing of whom you are meeting, what learning, and Beth and I hate you for it and shall instruct our children in hatred of you. My leisure has set affairs in motion again, the mail piles up, and word of our new availability has got round, with the result that we are too much abroad. Wherever I go I maintain my charm and radiate sweetness, and so shall I continue to do until after the Tenure crisis, when I shall revert, coil, and strike again.

Paul Purdy came Sunday with two actors. One played Lear, the other Tanner, during last year's University season, and we read the play into the tape, Lear reading Johnson, Tanner reading Boswell, Paul reading Britons and Scotsmen, I Americans, Beth whores and barmaids and ladies of fashion, all bringing (the actors, I mean, bringing) enormous insight and elucidation to their parts. Acting is a kind of discovery, as writing is for me, and I was amazed and delighted, even with my own prose, a rare experience for me. I have never heard Paul so enthusiastic. It's a really *very funny* play. I swear it. Say, does it ever occur to you, as you sit there ignoring my bell, that I might be a famous man some day—that some grubby, black-fingered Harold Rosenblatt in some cubicle of the future might be pawing his way through this very letter in search of a hint of my mystery? Yet you . . . you cast me aside, do not write me. Do you ever consider that *your* fame, your crumb of immortality, just *may* depend upon your inclusion in *The Collected Letters of Lee Youngdahl*? Can you so indifferent be?

Rosenblatt, Harold (1922-2016), friend; visits 123, 137, 437, 616, 873; mentions 653, 698, 744; to LY Sept 16 436; LY to numerously, esp. 329-31, 457-60, 515-18, 888; LY calls "grubby, black-fingered," charges indifference 888. See also Rosenblatt, Sylvia.

Meanwhile mortal,

Wednesday, October 10

[from Tremont C. Katt, Katt's Air College,
Monterey, California]

October 9

Dear Lee,

It's a lucky thing I was in the house when a telegram of condolence arrived from Whizzer so I could prevent Alice from seeing it. So you might as well know your stunt flopped. Don't deny it. I amn't dead. I won't be dead until the day I die. Have you given up jumping? Enclosed tickles me.

tom

[*enclosure from Katt*]

ITALIAN GIRL PLANS TO LEAP INTO MARRIAGE BY PARACHUTE

TURIN, *Italy* (UPI)—Eighteen-year-old Bianca Cappone loves Alberto de Cristofaro, a 36-year-old salesman, so much that she completed plans Saturday to leap into marriage with him—by parachute.

To please her prospective bridegroom, chestnut-haired Bianca will jump by parachute from a plane to the altar Sunday morning. So will Alberto and the priest who will marry them at an airfield ceremony.

For De Cristofaro and the priest, it won't be too bad. The groom is a former paratroop sergeant and the priest was the chaplain of his parachute regiment in World War II.

But for Bianca, it is a new experience. It will be not only her first wedding, but her first parachute jump.

For the occasion, she will be equipped with white overalls and a white crash helmet—with veil and orange blossoms attached.

[*from Abner Klang, New York*]

October 8 Lee as I predicted you have written a smash and we are on our way to a million. Enright con irms my opinion that you wrote a sensational play and mentioned Laughton and Olivier as Johnson and Boswell as both are English and wishes you inserted a leading lady.

I mentioned money without delay and told him you are no longer consenting not even to a man o his reputation to one year options. You will take a six month option as he readily agreed payable $1000 now and $1000 a ter three months less agency commission and a ter that he will either be in production or get o the pot subject to your satis action.

He will pay your trip to New York and put you up at a ine hotel and probably acquaint you with a lady or two in case you lost contact rom the last time and was pleased to hear you are not some long haired college variety airy. This is the kind o luxury treatment you could never get rom a dead end producer like T. T. Tattershall so I am telling you to put him out o your mind orever unless you have already done so as I hope. Never mention him again. I he contacts you knowing you inished your play tear it up and don't answer under any circumstances. Only a suggestion.

No play o Enright ever ran less than a year. The author o the book Bonanza Boat is based on is sitting around drawing about $5200 a week while the author o The amily Place is doing about hal the same. It is a drama. Enright wishes you didn't write it in one act but as I pointed out to him it is no trick to put an intermission in the middle or i he wants three acts put in two in the middle.

A ter all you are one o the inest writers and I want to tell you now in case I should God orbid die that you must never under estimate your own reputation. When I walked in there he hung out the red carpet. Lunch was $60. Your name is known and you are considered a bigger igure than many writers who are considered bigger igures. I might as well let my hair down and admit you always knew all along where the big money was. It is in the college reputation a ter all. I am so goddam anxious to see you I can't wait. Tell me what I can do or you and it is done. When I think o the way we have orged up the ladder together I bless the day we met although I know I will be sorry in the morning that I am giving mysel away like this instead o adhering to my normal nature and giving you the usual pitch how authors are made by agents. You would only know anyhow.

A business man decides he needs a little physical culture or his growing avoir du poise so he gets up every morning and runs around Central Park in his shorts and does a ew push ups and goes home to break ast. One day he runs and runs around the Park and does his push ups. He is doing his push ups near a bench a drunk is sitting on and the drunk watches awhile while the man in his shorts does his push ups going up and down and up and down and up and down on his hands and knees until the drunk says to him a ter awhile Shay there mishter, your riend le t.

Ever yours,

[*from Louis Garafolo*]

On Golden State Limited
October 9

Dear Lee,

I thought you might have been sore at me when I didn't hear from you so long. I was glad to be wrong when your letter arrived. I am now answering it.

I have a proposition that I know you'll be interested in when I tell you about. First of all I want you to see him fight Cottrell Friday night. If you could come down it would be fine, Alfred's Camp, 11311 Canton Drive, Studio City, but if you can't you will still get some idea on TV. TV is ruining the game. It drove it out of the professional clubs and in the house, and the quality is ruin. Watch his left hand. You won't see such a left hand on TV very often. The reason my writing is so shaking is because of the train. I am steadier than ever. If by any chance the tables turn against us Friday night I am going home and die a sad man. I say this because I am sure it won't happen.

The subject of what I want to talk to you about is money. Neighborhood of $3,000. He is not a big earner because he is not a free and open TV fighter. When he beats Cottrell he will move into Top Ten and even if not a TV fighter will start to earn. Finally quality shows. He is the best fighter in the country and one of the best I ever had. How is your wife and children and father and brother?

Don't quit your job because you always want the basic eats and flop. You can't do the big things every day but you have got to pay the rent every day and feed the breadsnappers. That is life. I know you can do the basic job with your little finger, keep your mind clear and stay in health.

[*to David Veenstra, San Francisco*]

October 10

My dear Bishop Veenstra,

I have been distressed to think (although it may be purely my imagination) that I may, in some manner, have been rude to you when, several weeks ago, you were kind enough to call upon me. At that time I was unwell: as you perhaps know, I have suffered for some time from Garafolo's Complaint, which has troubled the family for several generations, on mother's side.

Some of us have, as you eloquently phrase it, lost our way, moved too swiftly, perhaps, from the dry-farms of Utah to the rarefied atmosphere of the universities; intent upon the development of our intellect we have been careless, often, of the health of our spirit.

I am wondering, in this connection, whether Mr. Outerbridge might not be just the person to mediate, so to speak, the supposed dispute between my Church and me: he stands astride the worlds of faith and knowledge. He may be reached @ the English Department of the University.

Mr. Whizzer Harlow (@ General Delivery, Santa Fé, New Mexico), who is concerned to remain informed upon missionary matters of every sort, complains to me that he does not receive Church literature in sufficient quantity. Might he be placed upon your various mailing lists?

Faithfully,

Thursday, October 11

[*from Whizzer Harlow, Santa Fé, New Mexico*]

October 9

Youngdahl,

I went down in a canyon and I cried a little. I felt that I should be much more moved than I was, but I wasn't, and I went back up out of the canyon and looked for the relevant passage in The Life of Johnson but I couldn't find it so I read Lycidas instead. "Youngdahl," I thought, "would know the passage, or if not know it know how to find it," (where Johnson says he ate plum-pudding on the day a friend died) because Youngdahl keeps card files, because while I read a book and *love* it Youngdahl knows how to *use* it, because Youngdahl has all the luck, and everything he touches turns to gold, and when Youngdahl goes up in an airplane he jumps out with his son in his arms, and the pilot dies.

Can you lend me $50 more? I will never pay it back, probably.

What am I doing down here? I am starving to death with an Indian girl named Sally Parker. I have made love to girls on every continent except Australia, and of all the races of mankind, and in every clime, and in abodes of every type.

Whatever became of that association between you and that lovely big girl Cecile?

Use the key. I need the papers if I am to get any sort of a job, which I don't want, but must eat. I can't go along borrowing a dollar a day from Sally Parker, delighted as she may be to give it. I'm fairly adept at sleeping outdoors, but I'm no good at all at not eating, and if I don't get something in my stomach I can't write.

In Honolulu I fought in a sideshow, beating the ears off youths and drunks for $30 a day in the heat, and at night I wrote short stories about the basic brutality of romantics, all in long-hand because my typewriter gave out at last and I sold it for junk to pay for a tooth chipped away by a lucky drunk. It was a front tooth or I wouldn't have cared, but I am as basically vain as I am brutal and don't like girls with chipped front teeth and don't expect them to like me in the same condition.

I assume the play you finished was the Boswell play. You always finish what you begin. It is the Youngdahl luck. Nothing ever stops you, and I hate you, you always cut out a slice of the day and you said, "Out of my room," and you sat down with four sheets of paper and you banged away, clickety clickety clickety clickety and we all sat around the liquid and admired you sitting up there clickety clickety until you covered up your four naked sheets with your prose, and then—and only then—you came down and drank your drink, first always leaving behind you a record of your night, and I am standing up at the public P.O. writing with my bare hands because I sold my typewriter to buy a tooth or part of one, and you are sitting down with all your teeth.

I don't suppose I should mail it, but you always like to get down and sniff up the sewage of somebody else's emotions, and know how it feels like to be somebody you can't be. It may not be much, but it pleases Sally Parker.

Best of luck,

[*from Clinton Blalock, Harvard University*]

October 9

Dear Youngdahl:

Had I known, or been able to imagine, that you might willingly leave your seaside for ours I should certainly have preceded your inquiry with one of my own. Upon receipt of yours of the 3rd I called a quiet meeting of Youngdahlites here, few of whom can quite believe we shall ever actually have you, but all of whom are now engaged toward that ambitious goal.

The work before us entails principally the wooing of two key men, one of whom is, of course, Simonsen. Yet, forbidding as he may appear, his commitment to imaginative methods, and to the Johnson Period, places him squarely along the lines of probability.

You can aid us a bit, if you will, by sending me your *vita,* with emphasis upon your Boswell scholarship, some de-emphasis of your popular articles, perhaps light mention of fiction; by keeping us up-to-date on additional publication, and by apprising us of honors as they fall. I must say that I am astounded to learn that in the midst of all your other activity you have completed a play.

I saw a press item the other day to the effect that *The Hard Puncher* is to be dramatized on television, and you may be certain that I shall be at my set that night. It is as fine a work, in its special way, as *The Utah Manner,* although I suspect, as I piece together my information, and my image of you, that you prefer the maturity of the latter. Why don't you write a novel about the academic life?

With warm good wishes,

[*from Harry Searle, Larkspur, California*]

Dear Lee Youngdahl,

Enclosed please find another application blank. I believe I have quite a bit of influence at the members of The Dollar A Word Club and can manage to effectuate your membership in spite of your inability to meet the official requirements. Being quite frank with you, there are quite a few other members who do not meet them, either. In the blank requesting a reference from a member of the Club you may use my name, while in the blank requesting the name of the writing for which you received a dollar a word you may leave it blank. It should require only about two weeks to process your application and to notify you of membership, and you will be entitled to all the rights of duly elected members. We are all looking forward to having you as a member.

Our meetings are quite informal. We exchange market tips, eat heartily, bend the traditional elbow, and enjoy good fellowship, beginning promptly at one o'clock every Thursday, continuing for as long as we wish. It is quite a profitable experience in all ways. A number of our members, based on something heard or overheard, have gone away from our meetings with ideas for big sales, and once a year we have our annual Words And Music Banquet complete with our usual zany theme, which receives quite a wide coverage in the newspapers, and is attended by numerous leading editors from New York.

As a member you would be entitled to raise the question of our name during the portions of our meetings devoted to official business. Nobody has ever complained of our name before, but being a college professor I suppose you are quite a bit more alert on the matter. Please indicate on the blank whether we are supposed to call you "Dr." or not. If so, I know the members will do so. Maybe I just don't know what a compound adjective is, but everybody is quite used to it the way it is now.

Your mother would not be eligible for membership, as no women are allowed. Some of our conversation borders on the sort you wouldn't want your mother to hear. Wives are invited to the annual Words And Music Banquet, or as we say on the invitation "Wives or reasonable facsimiles."

I see by TV Trade Talk that Hard Punching is tapped for Window 9. I hope you got a good fee. You should have received at least $1,000 since it is your first time. Lester Young, incidentally a member, received $2,000 for a great job he did on Huckleberry Finn, and I received a similar amount for my adaptation of Les Miserable, the French story.

Looking forward to having you as a member,

[*enclosure from Searle, application for membership in* The Dollar A Word Club]

DIVISION OF EDUCATION

To: Dr. Lee W. Youngdahl
Department of English

From: Dr. Warren Eberhardt
Chairman, Committee on Instructional Evaluation
Division of Education

Date: October 10

Subject: In compliance with the Rules of the Committee on Instructional Evaluation, Division of Education, you are herewith furnished one copy of Memorandum October 10 describing distribution factors relative to Memorandum October 9. In compliance with the Rules of the Committee on Instructional Evaluation, Division of Education, you are herewith furnished one copy of Memorandum October 9 relative to advisory recommendations concerning University tenure.

Respectfully submitted,

cc: Office of President Stamish
Office of Dean Spohrer
Office of Dr. Gamble, Chairman, Department of English
Office of Dr. Purdy, Chairman, Committee on University Tenure, Department of English
Office of Dr. Conzett, Committee on Instructional Evaluation, Division of Education
Office of Dr. Waggoner, Committee on Instructional Evaluation, Division of Education
Office of Mr. Virdon, Department of Philosophy

Enclosures: Memorandum October 10
Memorandum October 9

[*enclosure from Warren Eberhardt*]

To: Dr. Lee W. Youngdahl
Department of English

From: Dr. Warren Eberhardt
Chairman, Committee on Instructional Evaluation, Division of Education

Date: October 10

Subject: In compliance with the Rules of the Committee on Instructional Evaluation, Division of Education, you are herewith furnished one copy of description of distribution factors relative to advisory recommendations concerning University tenure.

Distribution: Memorandum October 9 relative to advisory recommendations concerning University tenure has been distributed to the following:
Office of President Stamish
Office of Dean Spohrer
Office of Dr. Gamble, Chairman, Department of English
Office of Dr. Purdy, Chairman, Committee on University tenure, Department of English

Office of Dr. Youngdahl, Department of English
Office of Dr. Conzett, Committee on Instructional Evaluation, Division of Education
Office of Dr. Waggoner, Committee on Instructional Evaluation, Division of Education
Office of Mr. Virdon, Department of Philosophy

Respectfully submitted,

cc: Office of President Stamish
Office of Dean Spohrer
Office of Dr. Gamble
Office of Dr. Purdy
Office of Dr. Conzett
Office of Dr. Waggoner
Office of Mr. Virdon

[*enclosure from Warren Eberhardt*]

To: Dr. Lee W. Youngdahl
Department of English
From: Dr. Warren Eberhardt
Chairman, Committee on Instructional Evaluation
Division of Education
Date: October 9
Subject: In compliance with the Rules of the Committee on Instructional Evaluation, Division of Education, evaluation of the instructional methods of Dr. Youngdahl was undertaken relative to advisory recommendations concerning University tenure.
By Whom Conducted: The observational examination was conducted by Dr. Warren Eberhardt, Chairman, Committee on Instructional Evaluation, assisted by Dr. Thomas P. Conzett and Dr. Irene W. Waggoner, Committee on Instructional Evaluation, and Mr. Stanley Virdon, noncredentialized, Department of Philosophy.
When Conducted: The observational examination was conducted during the week April 16-20.

Rating Scale of Evaluation: Dr. Youngdahl was evaluated according to the French-Juega Numerical Rating Scale with Verbalized Equivalence.

Criteria Category: The criterial categories were: 1. "Dress and Appearance"; 2. "Clarity of Presentation"; 3. "Rapport With Student Group"; 4. "Essential Grasp of Materials"; 5. "Qualities of Leadership."

Evaluation

1. "Dress and Appearance." Dr. Youngdahl's dress and appearance are acceptable. In this criterial category he was evaluated as follows:

Dr. Eberhardt 86
Dr. Conzett 85
Dr. Waggoner 78
Mr. Virdon ...... no response

2. "Clarity of Presentation." Dr. Youngdahl does not show regular clarity of presentation. He does not always address his remarks to the student group, appearing to expect that the student group must accommodate itself to his level. He sometimes addresses his remarks to only a few, and is inclined to be impatient with those whom he considers to be thinking unresponsively. Occasionally he behaves contrarily to demands of a democratic learning experience by shouting at a student, "Wake up, stupid." In classes as large as his he fails to avail himself of microphonic or other audio-visual techniques, and when microphonic technique was suggested to him by one member of the observing group he replied in a discourteous and scornful

tone that he could never "see through a microphone."

He does not employ standardized texts but allows students to work from various editions, explaining that he is saving students money, but consequently many of the texts in use are immodern. Many students are using texts with small type. In a course such as Freshman 101, which is required to be standardized, students complain that the work is not comparable to the work given in other sections of that course.

There is no evidence of pre-planning. Often he appears without books, and seldom with notes, beginning his lesson in a dilatory way, often remarking upon the dress or appearance of members of the student group, and one day, observing that a student had dyed her hair, spent a great deal of time which might otherwise have been usefully employed in analyzing her motives. Written assignments are optional, Dr. Youngdahl arguing with the under-signed to the effect that it was not his desire to force students to write who did not wish to. His failure to pre-plan results in two classroom faults: 1) assigned material is not approached until the hour is under way, and 2) this results in the fact that the student group is never dismissed on time. Members of the Committee report that students leaving the room complain of lack of clarity of presentation in such language as, "I am now more confused than I was when I entered the classroom at the beginning of the hour," or, "I thought a great deal of time was wasted that might otherwise have been usefully employed." In this criterial category he was evaluated as follows:

Dr. Eberhardt	14
Dr. Conzett	20
Dr. Waggoner	25
Mr. Virdon	99

3. "Rapport With Student Group." Dr. Youngdahl's rapport with the student group is excellent. It was amazing to observe that in his discussions he knew all of his students by name, and revealed intimate bits of information concerning them. Although some express dislike for him ("conceited," "arrogant," "aggressive," "relentless," were some of the adjectives employed) the majority like him. Oddly, some of those who most vociferously dislike him are found to be among the most numerous instances of non-directive re-enrollment in his courses.

Attendance is high for the reason that he controls this factor in the following way. He destroys the card of a student who has been absent three times. (University regulations clearly state that no student card shall be destroyed.) Such action is arbitrary, fails to consider extenuating circumstances, and results in the failure of utilization of full building facilities. In this criterial category he was evaluated as follows:

Dr. Eberhardt	80
Dr. Conzett	80
Dr. Waggoner	75
Mr. Virdon	99

4. "Essential Grasp of Materials." His grasp

of materials is "apparently" very high, but since members of the Committee are non-specialized in the content area it is suggested that the criteria be declared non-criterial. He quotes memorizationally from numerous source materials. In this non-criterial category he was evaluated as follows:

Dr. Eberhardt 90
Dr. Conzett 90
Dr. Waggoner 85
Mr. Virdon 99

5. "Qualities of Leadership." Dr. Youngdahl has few qualities of leadership. His behavioral example is wholly undesirable. The atmosphere of his classroom is unsocialized, and procedural regularity is lacking. Students often may be seen carrying coffee cups to their seats, and many smoke in violation of prohibitionary signs. One student smoked a cigar. In his views and opinions he is inconsistent, thus affording a formative student group no clear model of attitudinal thought or behavior. In thought and language he is often disrespectful or vulgar, exhibiting a tendency to minimize all the accomplishments of national, civic, or educational institutions, and then in the space of one week reversing his entire position. Students frequently engage in unsupervised debate, as if no discussion-leader were available, Dr. Youngdahl merely engaging in this "cross-fire," waving his hands and shouting. Upon at least one instance some of his remarks were so contradictory to known facts that he was loudly booed and hissed by his more thoughtful students. In this criterial

category Dr. Youngdahl was evaluated as follows:

Dr. Eberhardt 5
Dr. Conzett 5
Dr. Waggoner 5
Mr. Virdon 99

Analysis of Ratings

Criterial Category 1:
Numerical Rating Scale: 83
Verbalized Equivalence: Excellent

Criterial Category 1 (in-calculation of one non-response):
Numerical Rating Scale: 62.3
Verbalized Equivalence: Good-excellent

Criterial Category 2:
Numerical Rating Scale: 39.5
Verbalized Equivalence: Low poor-unsatisfactory

Criterial Category 3:
Numerical Rating Scale: 83.5
Verbalized Equivalence: Excellent

Non-criterial Category 4:
Numerical Rating Scale: 91
Verbalized Equivalence: Superior

Criterial Category 5:
Numerical Rating Scale: 28.5
Verbalized Equivalence: Incompetent-very unsatisfactory

Overall Numerical Rating Scale: 65.1

Overall Verbalized Equivalence: High fair-good

Overall Numerical Rating Scale (out-calculation of non-credentialized observer): 27.0

Overall Verbalized Equivalence (out-calculation of non-credentialized observer): Incompetent-very unsatisfactory

Recommendation

The Committee on Instructional Evaluation, Division of Education, recommends that University tenure not be granted.

Respectfully submitted,

cc: Office of President Stamish
Office of Dean Spohrer
Office of Dr. Gamble, Chairman, Department of English
Office of Dr. Purdy, Chairman, Committee on University tenure, Department of English
Office of Dr. Conzett, Committee on Instructional Evaluation, Division of Education
Office of Dr. Waggoner, Committee on Instructional Evaluation, Division of Education
Office of Mr. Virdon, Department of Philosophy

[*to Whizzer Harlow, Santa Fé, New Mexico*]

October 11

Dear Whizzer,

The passage is this:

. . . Talking of our feeling for the distresses of others;—JOHNSON. 'Why, Sir, there is much noise made about it, but it is greatly exaggerated. No, Sir, we have a certain degree of feeling to prompt us to do good: more than that, Providence does not intend. It would be misery to no purpose.' BOSWELL. 'But suppose now, Sir, that one of your intimate friends were apprehended for an offence for which he might be hanged.' JOHNSON. 'I should do what I could to bail him, and give him any other assistance; but if he were once fairly hanged, I should not suffer.' BOSWELL. 'Would you eat your dinner that day, Sir?' JOHNSON. 'Yes, Sir; and eat it as if he were eating it with me. Why, there's Baretti, who is to be tried for his life tomorrow, friends have risen up for him on every side; yet if he should be hanged, none of them will eat a slice of plumb-pudding the less. Sir, that sympathetic feeling goes a very little way in depressing the mind.' (*Entered at Thursday, 19 October 1769.*)

So you may be relieved at not having been more depressed than you were, and I send you besides a plumb-pudding check for $50. I send you, also, as I have sent you before, a little memorandum of our transaction, which I request that you sign and send to Abner. Please! Abner says I must have documentation, for tax purposes, of uncollected or uncollectable monies. He doesn't say it so grammatically as I, but anyhow he says it, so oblige.

Now, if you will carry yourself to Mr. Hector La Paz, who lives on Camino del Monte Sol, he will give you a cabin, and food, and a typewriter, and he will move into your cabin a bed sturdy enough for both you and Sally Parker, and he will then withdraw from your life. You will hate him for all that he will do for you, and you will hate me more than ever for my assistance, but Hector is accustomed to being hated, and I am learning.

Everybody hates me here quite as much as you do, which, as a matter of fact, is why I have been wishing you wouldn't persist in the matter of the key: except in this, the autumn of my Tenure fight, a little honest housebreaking would appeal to me, for, if I were caught at it, the campus would resound with merriment. However, any such scandal at the moment would be disastrous. I am depending upon Paul Purdy to squeak me through, and I ought not to do anything which will make the task harder for him than it already is.

Anyhow, you must feel no compunction at taking from Hector whatever he offers, who is heir to $70-trillion his father earned, or anyhow accumulated, at the irrelevant sacrifice of two generations of Central-American banana workers. Allow Hector to be your symbol of capitalistic depredation, and he will allow you to abuse him as a means of relieving his guilt, and when you are tired of abusing Hector take your abuse to your cabin and pour it into prose. Don't waste your fingertips on angry letters. Write a story or an article or a novel about me—about what a really fiendish fellow I am.

I didn't know you were so down. I thought you earned good on the movie, which Beth and I and the Purdys and the Rosenblatts saw, and I was enchanted to see your name up there on the wide w——i——d——e screen, and I proudly said, "Why, I knew that lad when he thought it was mighty uncommon potatoes to hit the Sunday supplements." And every third line I heard Whizzer Heself laughing back there behind the wide screen, and I laughed, and Beth laughed, and the Purdys and the Rosenblatts, and nobody else in the theater laughed except us.

Afterward, when thought and logic settled in, Harold said he wondered whether it is the highest form of art for an artist to satirize his own labor, that all an artist does when he does *that* is to hoist himself to his own level again, so he can look himself in the eye again; which is (Harold said) only the point of beginning. He is at Yale this year, but what doing I don't exactly know—he won't write me—and Willa is pregnant again, and Paul will do my play after Christmas at University Theater.

Now that the play moves off paper to the flesh, and there is some option talk in New York, I find myself somehow addicted to visions of showgirls. Sam Johnson, you know, to guard himself from temptation, would never go backstage with Garrick. "I'll come no more behind your scenes, David; for the silk stockings and white bosoms of your actresses excite my amorous propensities." But I, with Boswell, am less particular, and always loved white. Boswell could, he said, "unite little fondnesses with perfect conjugal love." And I see New York out there across a bridge and a mountain and a desert, and more mountains and some rivers and finally another bridge, and there it is, "my whirlpool of curiosity," as Boswell called London, "my garden of delight." He stood at Highgate Hill, and he looked upon London, and he saw (this phrase alone might make a man his fame) "those mansions of gross sensuality." I shall take my visions and go, perhaps. Beth seems to favor the idea, which removes from it some of the thrill of risk.

Please don't forget to send Abner the little enclosure, and I thank you, and tell Hector I think continually of him who is truly rich.

Clickety,

[*enclosure to Whizzer Harlow*]

. . . .
date

I owe Lee Youngdahl $450.00

. . . .
autograph

[*enclosure to Whizzer Harlow, personal check, Bank of America,* $50]

Columbus Day. Friday, October 12

[*from Harold Rosenblatt, New Haven, Conn., postcard*]

October 7

Dear Lee,

I do wish you'd reply to my questions of my letter concerning the house. I thank you and send you all love in haste.

Kiss Beth and the kids,

[from Victor Wenk, special delivery]

WINDOW 9
Rockefeller Center
New York 20

October 11

Dear Lee—

In order not to take up too much of your valuable time—how does this sound—just a little note—in reply—will be perfectly satisfactory.

Hard Puncher comes out of the corner at the bell—Irishman comes out of the corner at the bell —Referee tells them to shake hands—and informs them that if anybody is knocked down—he must be up by the count of ten. THEN Hard Puncher says —"Let's start the fight and not waste any more time"—and the fight is on. But I want you to put this in Referee's lingo for us.

The idea is simple—that everybody agrees we can't eliminate the speech—we must afford the time—maybe fifteen seconds—because if the viewer loses the idea of the count of ten—if they don't have that information—we lose the suspense we built to while Hard Puncher is laying there—while Referee is counting.

Gabriella Bodeen quit the cast—new girl is even better—not so big. Rehearsals are coming along greatly. I'd very much apreciate a special delivery—or wire—to clear up this last little matter —of Referee's speech.

Gratefully,

[to Louis Garafolo, Alfred's camp,
Los Angeles, telegram]

SUPERB. HE WILL BE HEAVYCHAMP OF DE WOILD OR I AM SPAGHETTI AT DIMAGGIO'S WHEN YOU GET UP HERE AND ALL THE MONEY YOU CAN EAT. LOVE.

LEE

[*to Harold Rosenblatt, New Haven, Conn.*]

Columbus Day

Dear Harold,

> "For the black fumes which rise in your mind, I can prescribe nothing but that you disperse them by honest business or innocent pleasure . . ." (SJ *to* JB, *London, August 27, 1775.*)

What do you want to *know* about your house? It is there. I am looking at it this *instant*. Your renters, unless they are slinking about in the dark, are abed; fog plays about your chimney.

Beth and I sat in the sun this morning (one sharp eye, of course, upon your house, lest little children steal it), waiting for the mailman, who brought your card. Postmark: New Haven. "Now Harold will tell me," I thought, turning the card over, "that my play has arrived." Small, short, postcard-type sentences they shall be, I thought, but he will tell me his opinion of my idea for a Journal, and he will counsel me in my combat here, tell me whom he has met at Yale, and how my reputation stands thereat.

What a postcard it would be! What a postcard it was! I studied it for hours, brooded upon its ambiguities, rolled its magnificent periods on my tongue, savored its slow, developing metaphors, its memorable similes, its bright and shining turns and twists of phrase, its agile sallies, its dramatic climb, climactic fall, its breathless reversals of situation, its fearful plunges into black melancholy alternating with gay ascents into rising laughter. When I was done—when once again reality enveloped me—I knew afresh the meaning of the word *soul.*

(Statistical note: your card, exclusive of salutation and close, contains twenty-four words; I have just sent off a telegram containing twenty-six. Harold, dear fellow, why discharge all this emotion upon me? Am I really worth it? I am poor and weak. Economize. Save yourself, Sir. Give a little to your wife, your children, your work.)

At school I am asked what I hear from Harold. Now I shall tell them at The Coffee Bar, "Oh such a wealth I hear from him, such abundance of report," and I might even—don't you know—or would I dare? I mean, ornament it with a truth or two, for I am a story-teller and I must have a story to tell. In the absence of news, Harold, news must be made. "Poor Harold," they shall say. "He *did?* Really? When? How did it happen? Tell," and I see them now, the Bar, the waiting faces, the long table, my own countenance grave, my voice deep, steady, but subdued, and they shall inquire, "To the *brain?* Complete, total—to the brain, poor Rosenblatt, life is so unfair . . . taking Catholic orders? . . . divorce, and yet they always *seemed* so happy." "Well, the trouble was"—Youngdahl now, clinical, dispassionate, injury within bravely concealed—

"trouble was he got mixed up with a group of Yale rakes, and off they went, it's nothing much, penicillin licks it in hours, the 'mischief' as we call it in the Eighteenth Century, but the damn thing is he infected *Sylvia* . . ."

Don't let this happen to you.

Do you know that the Harbidges have insured every item of personal property they own—umbrellas, for example? At The Coffee Bar this morning I quick-produced a limerick.

A thrifty professor named Harbidge
Bought seventy tons of garbage.
He freely conceded
'Twas really not needed,
But he could not resist such a bargage.

He pretended to laugh, and he once again implored me, for the sake of my heirs, to join the various consumer leagues to which he belongs. "A man who insures his umbrella," I said, "can never be a good teacher." This he denied. "How, Sir," I asked, "can I spaciously create if I am to dwell upon pennies."

"We don't *dwell* upon pennies," he said. "We exchange information."

"About pennies," I said.

Mr. Gamble, who leads brigades of his own to bargain basements, sided with Harbidge, and I was unrestrained in condemnation of both of them. Harsh words were exchanged, I tossed and gored them, and the rival camps remain as before.

Definitely For Me	*Definitely Against Me*
Paul Purdy	Mr. Gamble
Clinch (manacled to Paul)	Harbidge
Mr. Outerbridge	

If I should go to New York on a little business trip, will you come down and spend a few days with me, or a week, or as long as you wish? If you prefer, we might rendezvous in Peekskill, which is about fifty miles north. My old fight manager will be there (I used to train there) with a new young fighter whom I just saw for the first time (tonight, on television), and who is a truly startling boxer with an imaginative left hand, whose strength, beauty, rhythm, and synchronized perfection I should endeavor to describe to you if ever I held out hope that you might yet be trained up to an appreciation of the art. He is a Negro, twenty years old. I shall remain long enough in New York to see him fight in November if I can talk myself into going. I tell Beth my absence ought to improve my chance for Tenure.

There are two shows on Broadway I wish you would see for me, and tell me just how bad they are; they are *Bonanza Boat* and *The Family Place,* and I should appreciate your comments, if you will oblige. You will also want to see Bodeen in *Sweet Girl,* and tell me if she is as good as I contend. On the subject of geniuses of one sex or the other, Whizzer Harlow is bouncing around down in Santa Fé, dashing through the mountains with tribes of

Indian girls and wondering why, somehow, my star has risen and his not. He says I have all the luck, which is to say I prefer, in solid old Mormon fashion, work to dissipation.

Now, homework. Boswell once said to somebody that something wasn't worth "two blue beans in a blue bladder." The line has remained with me. I tried in a number of ways to work it into the play, but it never fit. Now, however, a place for it occurs to mind, except I don't want to use it without knowing what it means. Beans? Bladder? Why blue?

In short, tell me *something,* and comfort me. Have a little Christian Jewish charity.

All here send trans-continental-Columbus-Day-type love,

Saturday, October 13

[*from Whizzer Harlow, Santa Fé, New Mexico*]

October 11

Youngdahl,

A card from Tom. Don't you know that a man doesn't enjoy exposure? Aren't you satisfied? Did you need some further evidence, one more footnote for your collection, to prove that any idle evening you can sit down with your four sheets of paper and make a fool of me? Your plaything, my expense. It is not the first time but it is the last, and you may enter it as such on your records, and show it to your boss and he'll promote you, and tell Mama and Papa and they'll put it in the Ogden papers, and go tell Tom I didn't really cry for him, and you will have one more friend and I will have one more enemy, and soon you will have them all, and I will have none. Tell all the little boys and girls when they come running to hear the Great Words from the Great Tongue of the Great Youngdahl. At night I dream I'm punching you, you're way up there and I'm way down here, and I have killed you a thousand nights.

I never told a lie in my life. Sally Parker has left me. It is an old story, and it always hurts, but the truth is, in the world where the Youngdahls thrive, that lies are always assumed, and my truth then, too, is assumed to be a lie, and when I told her the truth she deducted the usual, and she's gone back to her wigwam now. I don't stand a chance, and I've given up expecting, but the one thing I've expected is that my own few friends will keep the record straight for me. Friends are truths, and when they cease to be truths they cease, too, to be friends. You who are dedicated to preserving! Ah, scholarship! Ah, meticulous footnote! Shall we not check and re-check, gentlemen, the exact hour of the ancient day, check hard, check hard, and we will be full professors quicker than you can say (in Latin, please) Jack Robinson. I never promised Sally or any other girl marriage or money or even love. I always said, "Soon I move along," and if that was how they wanted me, for the clean bed and the warm moment, which was all I ever promised, it was how I could be had. And I never promised friendship unless I could deliver, and in that way was I toward you, and for my truth you give me lie. So let's, just in case we ever by some accident I promise you I'll try to avoid, happen to come face to face, let's just walk right on past.

Please send the key to me, or since I have no use for it to my loathsome wife.

[to Tremont C. Katt, Katt's Air College,
Monterey, California, postcard]

Tom Katt's obituary Tom Katt denied.
"I amn't dead,"
Tom Katt said,
"And I won't be dead till the day I've died."

[*to Harold Rosenblatt, New Haven, Conn., postcard*]

This morning as I was strolling with the kids past your house, on the way to the mailbox to mail a letter to you, we happened to glance toward your house and to notice, when, I mean, we glanced, the children and I, as we walked, your letter in hand (it was quite a coincidence), that it, which is to say your house, had, during, I assume, the night, burned completely to the ground.

LWY

[to Whizzer Harlow, Sante Fé, New Mexico]

October 13

Dear Whizzer,

I have given away a perfectly good ticket to a perfectly good football game to spend my day brooding over your letter; and then (in my contemptible way, for my file-cabinet you have always despised, and my wicked habit of retaining carbon copies) I have reviewed our recent correspondence with the end in view of discovering why I told the particular lie I told.

I find it strange to be told, by a man who earns his living writing make-believe, that I must not lie, and stranger still to discover that he believes I lied to "prove" something or other. Do you really believe in *intent?* If you do then you, much more than I, resemble the academic critic—I mean of the poorer sort—and the journalistic reviewer: the poor critic supposes intent, and the writer laughs.

Checking and re-checking the date of my letter to you against my private diary and my memory (I shall be a full professor yet), tracing my movements, I discover that I had just come from your wife, for I had struck upon the daring scheme of approaching her directly for the documents you request, instead of breaking into the house. It is not a happy house. I did not stay long. Your boy looked too longingly upon me, with eyes too solemn.

If possible, no boy should be without a father. This is not to say that a boy should have *you* for a father, for that would convert solemnity to pathology, but you should have contemplated this matter some time ago, and you should have put it back in your pants unless you were prepared to assume the responsibility of so great a pleasure as I am sure it must have been: for she is very beautiful, wise, and animated, and I might have kissed her as I left had not your boy been there, and two of mine.

And so, instead of kissing her, I came home and wrote without at all planning it (critics never believe this sort of thing) and surely without any conscious intention of rendering you unhappy, or of shaming you, a little story which seemed to me, at the time, to be about myself and Earl and how we made an imaginary jump, which is the only way, you see, we *can* jump, because otherwise I'd have Beth and the P.-T. A. on my head.

The climax of the story is Tom Katt's death. (There's a sentence any of a hundred stolid critics might have written.) Need I be merely factual to tell you that Tom Katt soon shall die? Must I be bound by Time? Upside down he likes to fly, and when that becomes boring he flies upside down blindfolded, and when the thrill is gone he flies upside down blindfolded and drunk, and upside down blindfolded and drunk no-hands, and at last upside down blindfolded drunk no-hands with girls who badly enough want a pilot's license to allow Tom, in exchange for free lessons, to fly upside down blindfolded drunk no-hands screwing at the same time. This is Tom's conception of widening "experience." Neither he nor you will ever understand that the most rewarding experience a man can know is the experience of relating to his society, doing his work, and passing life down to the future no worse than he found it.

Did I strike too close to you? Did I summon up within you reflections upon the various and colorful ways in which a man might contrive to cast away his useless life, and leave behind him ladies laid but never loved, and a solemn son, and a wife alone, and take with him a talent whose highest achievement was once, in a B-picture, to mock a film nobody had taken seriously in the first place? I am a thrifty Mormon farm-boy, and I hate waste.

Times when you were here, and full of all your talk of all your girls on all your continents, you were Boswell and I your Temple: "My friend Temple is a man of much reading, especially since he was married. He says to me in a late letter, 'You will be surprised and vexed to find how much knowledge I have acquired'." So I tried to enliven myself, make myself more manly in your eyes, and I enumerated my conquests, most of which were fictitious—all but Cecile, whom I shall not discuss now—all fancy, all imagination: no more polygamy, we Mormons declared, not because it wasn't fun but because it was best for Utah that each man have only one wife. Thus was strife and distraction reduced, and all energy diverted to the paths of creation and economy. Instead of flying upside down continent to continent I went upstairs and clickety clickety clickety, wretch that I am.

Yes I am, too, you son of a bitch, and don't you forget it, either, because (listen! here are my crimes now) I've raised and fed a family indoors and haven't the slightest intention of abandoning the old Boswell-Scotch-Johnson-English-Youngdahl-Utah idea that every man, if he be a man, barters a part of his freedom so that the world of children might survive.

No, Sir, do we ever meet again we shall not "walk right on past." Rather, I shall bash you in the mouth, so that you will not attempt, at the cost of some other man's child's free running, to lure or tempt a proper worker from his proper labor.

If this letter proves as useful to you as it has been to me I shall feel doubly paid, second serial rights on top of the first. It is the Youngdahl luck. My God how the money rolls in!

Sunday, October 14

[to Clinton W. Blalock, Harvard University]

October 14

Dear Blalock:

Your most encouraging letter of the 9th is here, and I hasten to tell you that our Department secretariat has sent you a list of my publications, honors, kudos, and other propaganda designed to present me in a favorable if mis-leading light. Underneath, I am a scoundrel and a blockhead, and I trust you are the same.

My colleagues here have the somewhat premature notion that I am off to you—that Harvard has already asked me—a notion I attempt to clarify, mostly with the result that I receive additional praise for my presumed modesty. Yet I am not at all modest. I tell the truth, and even, in instants of exuberance, am all too likely to stretch it. However, in the present case I am not responsible for rumor.

I thank you most sincerely for your kind words about *The Hard Puncher* and *The Utah Manner.* You are astute to divine my preference for the latter, although even that book now fails to satisfy me: when, my stomach allowing, I turn pages in it, I wince at its bad style, and I see so plainly its transparent young manhood, its playing out of my old complaint against the home folks—who, now

I see them better, appear to me to be quite what I am becoming. My son, Lucien, throws a ball this bright afternoon against the house, and I lean from the window and cry, "You'll break the window," and he says he won't, and he is quite positive he won't, as I was quite positive, no matter how many I broke, that I wouldn't; he is as positive now as I was then that father is a fool.

The Utah Manner is less naive, I think, than *The Hard Puncher,* which was also the spinning-out of an amendment to a disappointment of the past: for I was at one time seized by the more or less realistic ambition to be Heavyweight Boxing Champion of the World. Clad in a gladiatorial robe across whose back, in vast golden script, was written,

—sewed there by my mother, who believed in me because my father said so—I set off into the world of gymnasia, beat up all the amateurs in Utah, beat up all the amateurs in the Mountain States, beat up all the amateurs in the New York Golden Gloves, and was plucked from the many by a prize-fight manager who saw very well how hard I hit with either hand, and how I was myself amenable to punishment, but who did not know that I was, upon the inside, becoming less and less the fighter, and more and more the social reformer. It had begun to appear to me less than purposeful to go about in life cracking the skulls of poor colored boys and poor Irish boys and poor coal-mining boys whose allies I should rightly have been. My slowly declining interest resulted one sad night in the fight that was my last—in, as a matter of fact, Boston—where a poor Irish boy, with not much gratitude for my pro-Irishism, and who was not half the fighter I was, bloodied me badly. That fight I have fought over again ten thousand times in my mind, and I won it at last in *The Hard Puncher,* thus discharging my hallowed sorrow.

What I started to say was that I hope you will not take the trouble to watch *The Hard Puncher* on TV. It is not he but someone else. When the papers were signed I was in the midst of my play, and I said, "Go ahead, you louse it up, leave me alone," and it was grandly loused.

(You won't believe this, and I really can't, in the slightest, blame you, but Lucien has just broken another window.)

Subject, of course, to approval by my Chairman, I shall be making a trip on literary business to New York about the end of the month, and I should certainly be pleased, if Simonsen were free, to meet with him or with any other interested Harvardites. My agent, Abner Klang (SC. 6-6277), will be charged with blocking out my time. His first tendency will be to reject you upon the grounds that you are neither a millionaire Hollywood producer nor a millionaire Broadway producer nor a millionaire magazine editor, so you must talk tough to him, tell him I said you *cannot* be denied, and he will respond. I would tell him myself, but he cannot remember anything unless it first be notarized and legalized, an option paid and the check clear. All must be, as he often says, "bonified," which you will easily recognize as the past participle of the verb "to bonify: I bonify, he bonifies; a conference is held toward the end of bonifying by the process of bonification, etc." A friend of mine once said a pretty thing of Abner. "Abner," he said, "promised me faithfully, and he will if he remembers."

With which I now depart you to search for a glazier open on Sunday. "I asked Johnson whether I might go to a consultation with another lawyer upon Sunday . . . JOHNSON. 'Why, Sir, when you are of consequence enough to oppose the practice of consulting upon Sunday, you should do it: but you may go now. It is not criminal, though it is not what one should do, who is anxious for the preservation and increase of piety, to which a peculiar observance of Sunday is a great help. The distinction is clear between what is of moral and what is of ritual observation'."

Is the repair of a window ritual or moral? Am I of consequence enough? Resolve this doubt, Sir, for him who petitions to remain your pious but doubtful and bewildered servant,

October 14

Mr. Harry Searle
Larkspur, California

Dear Harry Searle:

Herewith I return to you my completed application for membership in The Dollar A Word Club, although, as I have said, I am really not quite eligible. Maybe soon, though, I shall be! Here's hoping, eh?

Yesterday a very distressing thing occurred at the football game. A quite seedy looking man came up to me and asked, "Are you Lee Youngdahl?" and when I said I was he thrust the enclosed scrawl into my hand. Then he disappeared, and I later tried to re-locate him and give him quite a talking to, but I could not. He wore a brown overcoat. My wife says such an occurrence is quite shocking, and she was quite shocked to read the "poem." As a University professor I was also quite shocked both at the content of the "poem" and its bad literary style: it is not a good poem, its title is too long, the word "chuckling" doesn't rhyme with anything, and it can't be sung in the first place to the tune of "Way Down Yonder in New Orleans," for I have tried.

What can be done about things like this? I think it is jealousy, don't you? Do you have any suspicions who might have written it? For example, any enemies you may have, who are no doubt quite bitter at not being invited into The Dollar A Word Club? You know how jealous writers are!

What would be the chance of your coming out to the University and speaking to one of my classes? I have a course designed for students interested in writing, and from time to time I invite guest speakers to appear. Last year, for example, Lester Young (a Dollar A Word Member) consented to speak, and we had quite a lively session, I can assure you. I am sorry that I cannot offer you much of a fee, but the English-Department budget does allow me to pay you a small honorarium of $25, and you will honor me by being my guest beforehand at The Faculty Club for luncheon. I'd like to suggest either a Tuesday or a Thursday this month, or in December. I suppose you'd prefer a Tuesday, since Thursday is Club day, but suit yourself. Do not trouble yourself to prepare extensive remarks, but merely speak, merely *be yourself*, so that the students may have the best possible opportunity to absorb your point of view. Last year Lester Young helped to drill quite a bit of sense into our youngsters out there, so many of whom have quite dreamy and idealistic notions of literature, whereas what we try to do is bring them back quite a bit toward the *practical* side of things, and let them hear from really successful writers how the old game goes.

Yours very sincerely,
Dr. Lee W. Youngdahl

[*enclosure to Searle*]

LINES WRITTEN A FEW MILES SOUTH OF LARKSPUR, CALIFORNIA

(after reading in the *Chronicle* that Harry Searle says that all worth-while San-Francisco writers are members of The Dollar A Word Club—or else belong to "The Beat Generation." "Writing," says Searle, "is just a business, like any other.")

TO BE SUNG TO THE TUNE OF
"WAY DOWN YONDER IN NEW ORLEANS":

"Why do you pass," Harry was asked,
"Gas through your mouth?
"Are you perverse?"

"No, just reverse," Harry replied, genially
chuckling.
"Which is to say,"
Harry added, warily meditating,
"That the gases where my mouth is
"Seeped up from where the South is,
"While the brain displaced by gases
"Dropped to where an ass's
"Brains are said to be."

CHORUS:

"WAY DOWN YONDER IN NEW ORLEANS."

—*Anon.*

[enclosure to Searle]

Application For Membership
THE DOLLAR A WORD CLUB
San Francisco
California

Name. Lee. W. Youngdahl, Ph.D.
Address. 105 Yukon Street, San Francisco 14.
Telephone.
Business Address. University.
Business Telephone.
What article, story, or other item of yours has ever been purchased at the rate of at least $1 per word or more? None.
By whom Invited. By Mr. Harry Searle.
Date of Place of Birth. July 24, 1847, when the first Mormon contingents arrived at Ogden, Utah. (Pioneer Day annually celebrated on this day.)
Date of Application. October 14.
Religious Affiliation. None at present.
How long have you been writing? Fifteen years.
State in one hundred words or less why you wish to become a Member of the Club? In my work as a University professor I don't get to meet people out of that circle. I'd like to get out and meet people concerned with literature, and exchange market

tips with them, and enjoy good fellowship, for it sounds to me like quite a profitable experience. I might pick up story ideas at the Club and after awhile write a novel with all the members as characters, as James Boswell did, telling people how everybody talked and behaved and raised Hell. (83 words.)

Specialties. (For example, are you an amateur magician? Sing? Have you ever sung in a barber shop type quartet?) I am quite sorry to say I am not an amateur magician, but I can sing, as Boswell sang, "with great gusto," my particular specialty being Scotch catches, most of which can be sung at the annual Words And Music Banquet when ladies will be present. I can also tell lusty jokes and tall tales, and when I was younger I was quite a fair professional boxer, so I guess you could just call me "a regular fellow." (I fought 33 fights and won all but the last.)

Monday, October 15

[*from Whizzer Harlow, Santa Fé, New Mexico*]

October 13

Dear young Olddahl,

Much touched am I by yours of the 11th with the 50 Bank of American Dollars and the IOU which I've sent on to Abner, and your quotes from Johnson and Boswell with all the quotation marks inside quotation marks in single and double as they taught you to do in all your universities and as you are now teaching the new generation to do until soon all life will be perfectly punctuated. But what will they know of pain and hope and love and spirit? Do you teach anything called The Fundamentals of Illusion or Advanced Anguish?

Over the weekend I move into the estates of Hector La Paz, cozy cabin fireplaced, pinon stacked by serfs, wine on the mantle and a big broad bed and a shining black typewriter and white paper, and I'll see what I can create, I to be joined there by a Spanish girl barefoot, whom I have not touched and whose name I scarcely know, whom I met upon the dusty road and said, "Whither, little Spanish girl with barefoot feet?" and she replied "Nowhere" in a little barefoot voice, and her teeth white-sparkled, and I said, "Come then with me," and so she did. It was mute. Speech we do not need, nor punctuation, when there are eyes and hands and presence.

My Hollywood money? It went about one third to the United States Government for taxes past and present and future to blow up Japanese fishermen with in the interests of your academic science, and one third to the State of California for alimony past and present and future for my foul wife that was, and ten percent to Abner for getting me the job. That answers your question. Now answer mine about Cecile. I think she is as gorgeous a creature as ever I espied, and big, like you like them. Do professors appreciate such? Is she not wasted upon the academic air? She recalls to me New York days, and giant girls we knew. Where are they now? Married or rich, dead, mothers, harlots, some to penthouses, some to suburbs, to mansions and mental hospitals, Bodeen to fame, some too fat, too thin, diet, exercise, renovate your face, head of new hair, mouth of factory teeth, spectacles, and oldish photographs proving that what is now true was not always true, old films, old scrapbooks, old playbills, and we shall go then, you and I, whenever you say, and capture new giants come to town who were virgins back in South St. Cedar Fork when their big sisters were losing it to you and me, and I shall hope there will be forever and ever sisters and daughters of the giants for me, and daughters of the sisters and daughters, and I shall die in convulsions of sheerest ecstacy when there are nine times nine in candles on my cake. Meanwhile I'm going to see if I can't make some money on Hector's typewriter.

Is there really any kind of money in a San Francisco show? But Purdy, and Harold, they were never my dish of tea, nor do their opinions of my picture work in the least way touch me. Their hearts are stones. What passes in Harold for intellect is a mumbo-jumbo. His usual method of defending his position is to tell you he can't understand your terms. He and I once scrapped over a story of mine (later grabbed by The New Yorker) which he said lacked reality, my defense being (why did I bother?) that I touched at least spirituality, but this he pretended not to understand, and he asked me where spirituality was and what it was made of, and I said it was here, my heart, and spirit is spirit is spirit is spirit, love is love is love, and hope is hope is hope, and I am I am I am I, and you are you are you, and I implore you always to be you and never he who is an X-ray technician's third assistant helper.

I send you love, spirit, wine, the odor of pinon,

[*from Bishop Veenstra, San Francisco*]

October 13

Dear Leland,

I have received many letters from many young men seeking a way, but no letter has ever inspired me more than yours, and when I showed it to Mrs. Veenstra she said, "What an inspiring letter it is." Mr. Outerbridge was also inspired, and suggested to me that all matters should await until after you have more fully recovered from your ailment, perhaps the Christmas season. I agreed with him that a time of awaiting and reflection is wise for many reasons, and will you kindly tell me if you like this decision.

About your question, it never seemed to me that you were in some manner rude at all, but very courteous, and as Mr. Outerbridge suggested your imagination ran away with you. Then when I know that you were also ill of Garafolo's Complaint this adds to my sympathy for you. Sickness and illness make men short, as I am able to know in my rounds among the sick and ailing daily.

As you suggested to me I am sending Church literature in sufficient quantity to Mr. Whizzer Harlow, General Delivery, Santa Fe, New Mexico, and am also adding your name to the lists as Mr. Outerbridge suggested. Yours with the kindest regards, and God's blessing to you and your family here and your family home.

Faithfully,

[*from his mother, Ogden, Utah*]

Columbus Day

Lee Dear,

You didn't mention if you want the chiffanear or not. I don't think Dee wants it, Jeannie decided, and Dee says we can chop it in half and he will take half if you will take the other half. That Dee!! Daddy is at Dee's watching the fights, and Daddy tried to write "a little note to Mr. Outerbridge as you asked.

But he tore it up. He is afraid to write Mr. Outerbridge because he is afraid he will laugh at his writing, although he doesn't say so, but I know. It is nice of him to remember us. Sometimes you wonder who remembers you.

Why don't you write a little note to Dee? Dee says Bobby and Giff want a signature from Red Traphagen.

Lee Dear, I am not upset about anything that happened between you and Mr. Veenstra, or Bishop, and Daddy isn't upset either, but he may be a little more upset than I am. But I know that there are differences in people, and you are not like all the boys, and some people agree better with the atmosphere of the church.

I am glad you like the little gift for Tetsey. It was only a thought.

In your letter we are all a little mixed up where you say you finished your play, and then you say you didn't write it. Are there two plays? If there are two plays it is no wonder you are tired, or as you said "in a state of nervous prostration.

In exactly two weeks from tonight everybody will be crowded around their television. It will be a great night for the *home town boy!!* And are we proud!! It seems that you weren't too fond of the adaptor. What was his name? Be more patient, Dear, he did his best. Dee teases me by saying he will watch the fights instead of your play, but he is only teasing.

Lee Dear, tell me about the chiffanear, and kiss Beth for me, and squeeze every one of the children for me, and kiss them for me, the tightest squeeze and hug you can, and if Lucien won't let you then do it when he is asleep, and tell them it is from me, the proudest Mother and Grandma that ever lived. Lee Dear, Good Night, and don't tire. Rest more.

All love,

[*to Harold Rosenblatt, New Haven, Conn., postcard*]

Today (Octo 15) as, in the company of my one-time manager, and the distinguished young gentleman who will be the next Heavyweight Champion of the World, and whom, as white men once owned black, I, to the extent of 12½%, own, I was driving past your house, I happened to observe several seafaring men carrying it away, whereupon, slowing, inquiring, I was told it was not a heavy house, and therefore they wanted it, for they were in need of a lighthouse. LWY. (Mutual friend of ourn tells me you heart stone. Is true?)

[*to Abner Klang, New York, N. Y.*]

October 15

Dear Abner,

I shall arrive in New York on or about Saturday the 27th in order to see a prize-fight November 16. There is no reason why, in the interim, I should not transact a little business so long as it does not obstruct my pleasure.

I do not demand much, but what I demand I expect. I assume, therefore, that you will study carefully my outline of desires. Collect yourself. Try to visualize these not as multiple desires but as a single general plan embracing a unified end.

First let me ask you to search your files or floors for the conclusion to the promising joke begun in your letter of October 5. Then go phix your typewriter. No, wait!

New York desires:

1. That was a nice, neat, discreet hotel I stayed at last time, but I do not want, again, a rear room. Brick walls bore me. Streets interest me. Silence I do not want: if I did, why would I go to New York when I could go to Utah?

I do not want television in my room, but telephone calls I will receive from eleven until noon, with breakfast in bed.

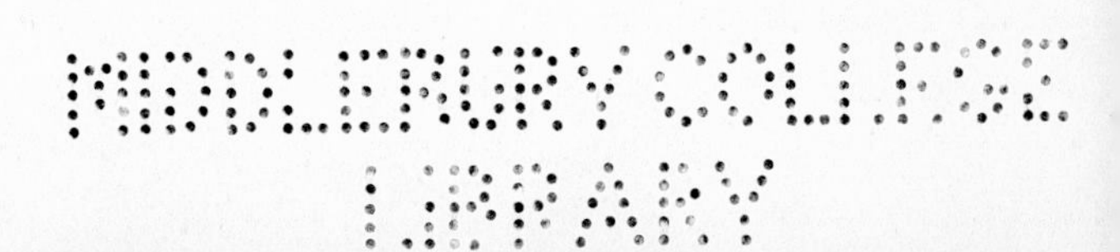

I want a typewriter in my room, preferably one of those old-fashioned machines with the 26-letter alphabet. (I might add, at this point, that I expect, before you write one more letter on my behalf, you will cause that typewriter to be repaired.)

2. I do not wish to see anybody from the publisher. When I have written a book I will send it to them. When I have not written a book I have, with them, no business.

3. I do not wish to see any magazine editors. When I have written a story or article I will send it to them. When I have not written a story or article I have, with them, no business.

(N. B. I am not a manufacturer but a writer, and I live by spontaneity, not by plan. I do not think before I speak. I do not plan before I act. I do not look before I leap. If you can understand this well enough to convey the idea to editors I shall be as gratified as I shall be open-mouthed. Why I trouble to write it I am not sure: I attribute my quixoticism to two thousand years of Western Romanticism.)

4. I shall be overjoyed to see anyone representing Harvard University. Give them all the time they want.

5. I shall be overjoyed to see anyone traveling under the name Harold Rosenblatt, of Yale. Give him all the time he wants.

6. There shall be waiting for me at the hotel, please, a time-table showing connections on the New York Central Railroad between Manhattan and Peekskill.

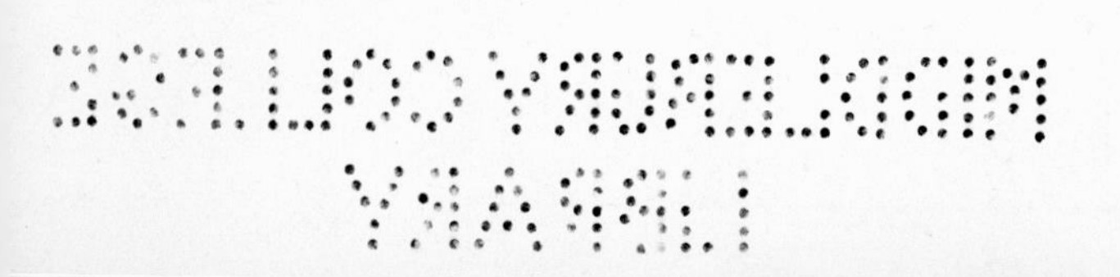

Desire 6, Sub-desire A: I have just bought, for $3,000, a 12½% interest in a prize-fighter named Alexander Irwin, who will be training at Peekskill. In this connection, I shall be pleased to be interviewed by representatives of reputable newspapers and/or magazines. Please arrange all interviews for lunch, to be taken in small restaurants during the off-hours, or for dinner, likewise late but *never to extend later* than the hour at which the cast of *Sweet Girl* is dismissed. Please check times on this.

Desire 6, Sub-desire B: You must advise these people of the press that I have come to New York at the request of Heavyweight Irwin and his aides to instruct him as he prepares to fight Ike Sanzobo on November 16. It's always fun to have a little publicity, which makes me the envy of my friends, who pretend to scorn the newspapers. The news angle—the human interest—is this: here's Lee Youngdahl, college professor, author, ex-fighter, controversial Mormon, vaulted cross-country to the principal literary seat and center of the greatest nation upon the face of the earth—and *why?* To execute literary contracts? To consult with other erudite professors? Yes, partly, but, *principally,* to instruct his prize-fighter in the art of success.

End of desires.

Since Enright is paying for this little jaunt I suppose we must give him some time. I expect that his first motion in my presence will be to hand me a check for $1,000, covering travel. Then I shall be anxious to see *Bonanza Boat* and *The Family Place,* and to read scripts of shows he has produced in the past. (If, however, his shows dismiss less early than *Sweet Girl* I shall prefer matinees.)

Now, in your advance dealings with Enright the details are not nearly so important as the image of me which you present to him. I worked thirteen months on that play, poured into it years of scholarship, brought to it all I know, at the moment, of life and craft. Enright will be, because of his financial talents, a splendid man to produce it. But he must, from the first, be impressed with the fact that he is producer only: I am the playwright. (This television experience with Window 9 has been enormously informative to me—the first known example of educational television.) His job is to supply money, rent a theater, engage ticket-takers. When he has engaged a director approved by me it will be the task of the director—*not* the task of the producer—to proceed with the artistic conception. (I should like to see, incidentally, any shows directed by directors Enright may be contemplating for *Boswell's Manhattan Journal.*) The separation of art from business is as crucial as the separation of church from state, or land from sea.

He is not a man of much good taste. He is not a man of wisdom. He must know that there comes to him now, out of the West, one who, in the deep recesses of sequestered universities, and by magic processes unknown to persons holding less than three degrees (and a fourth honorary), has intensively studied in numerous obscure languages the secret of the drama from the Greeks and Calvary to George Bernard Shaw. Tell him I am Phi Beta Kappa, and my wife, too, of my intimate association with scholars burrowing at Yale and Harvard into the most abstract unworldly data. My mind, he must know, is an impenetrable mystery. Attribute to me any derogatory remark you care to invent to support my instinctive opinion that his is a golf ball.

He knows, Abner, how very unwise he really is, but he doesn't know that anybody else knows, for he is surrounded by flatterers. If you don't do this we are going to be put to the trouble of locating another producer, time will have been wasted, and you, my good man—think of this!—will have lost money.

As for a leading-lady to be "inserted," the single act to be separated into two or three—all this is not only demented but precisely the sort of thing which must be banished from Mr. Enright's province. If he cares to watch a lady who, playing the role of First Whore, will do for my play what Bankhead did for *The Skin of Our Teeth,* have him see Gabriella Bodeen in *Sweet Girl.* The part was written with her in mind. Laughton would be, I am sure, a splendid if obvious Johnson, but Olivier no Boswell: but the play does not need "names" nor Englishmen, only *actors and actresses,* if any be left undemolished by a theater which has ceased to make demands upon them, people full of fire and longing who, with one immense effort, might bring our stage up again a little way along the road to reality.

I want no part of feasting or celebrities or night-clubbing or riding around in taxicabs through the splendor of your village, no "whores and bottles and pots of beer." I wish to be left, once dinner is done, alone, to prowl and listen and fill my well again.

All right, begin. Work carefully. Rely upon what you have studied, but use, too, common sense when you do not know the answer. Don't look at your neighbor's paper because he may be stupider than you are: you may not think such a thing is possible, but then you just haven't graded as many examinations as I have.

Desirously,

Tuesday, October 16

[*from Dee Youngdahl, Ogden, Utah, undated*]

Dear Lee,

Alexander Irwin has the best left hand I ever saw. He also has a strong right hand, but it is not the best I ever saw. However, it is better than anybody else's right hand. When I noticed Cottrell was drifting to his left I was wondering why he was doing so. Dad said Irwin was hitting him harder with the left hand than the TV showed, and we shoved up and looked a little closer. It is hard to see all the fine points, but I could see Irwin was hitting him with unusual power. Garafolo has the best fighter he ever had.

Cottrell had good courage, but he knew that he was beat. He tried to cover this fact with footwork but by the end of the second round he could not fool Irwin. Maybe he thought he might hit Irwin with the right over the left, but he could not, and there was nothing left for him but keep drifting to his left and hope Irwin dropped dead from a heart attack. You can't win by drifting.

Right in the middle of the third round Dad said it was about time Irwin hit him with the right hand if he had any. We were so impressed watching the left hand we both forgot all about the right. So did Cottrell.

I have to laugh seeing in the papers writing concerning the power of Irwin's right hand, but the power is in the left hand. The left hand murdered Cottrell, and when he was dead the right hand buried him. I hope you are not as dumb in your writing as the writers that write the boxing in the papers. The papers say he is a machine, but he is not a machine. He has a smart brain, and he uses it. He knew to wait for the exact second to use his right hand, and then he used it. I see him listening to Garafolo. He has the brain to listen. All fighters do not have the brain to listen, for example you did not. Garafolo might have told him what to do, but he could not tell him what exact second to do it. When he was alone up there he had to know for himself. If he missed he could have been hit bad with Cottrell's left. There is no such thing as the three minute round, but only the four minute round. In the fourth minute you are listening to the man in your corner. A machine does not listen. It was the best brain and timing.

I am sorry for Cottrell. He came up the long, hard way and I wonder what he is going to do now. But somebody must win. Irwin will beat Sanzobo and go to the title. If you are ever in touch with Garafolo congratulate him for me.

We are all fine here and will be looking at your TV show. Hoping to see you Thanksgiving.

[*from Harry Searle, Larkspur, California*]

October 15

Dear Lee,

I am quite overjoyed to have your completed application, and I am going to speed it through the Membership Committee without delay. You will find the Club quite a profitable experience for you, and you won't regret in the slightest joining us in weekly fellowship.

I don't know exactly who wrote that poem, but I have quite a few suspicions. That kind of thing doesn't bother me any more, although it used to. I don't give that kind of thing a thought any more. It might have been written by a so-called Club Member for all I know, where there is quite a bit of jealousy among the members, as there is bound to be in any organization of that type, or it might have been written by a member of the Beat Generation, and it is the sneaky kind of thing a man must put up with. Let a man tell me to my face what he thinks, because I don't mind honest criticism, but not go sneaking around at football games.

I will be quite happy to come out to the University and talk to your class. If I can't make a better speech than Lester Young, although a close personal friend as well as member, I'll be mighty ashamed of myself. Just name the day, Tuesday or Thursday perfectly suitable. If it's a Thursday we can have lunch at the Club first, or afterwards, or a drink, depending upon your time commitments, and I can show you off to fellow Members.

However, I cannot accept a fee, so why not take the $25 and apply it to another speaker or some good cause, the reason being that my taxes are already quite high. I'll let you in on a little something. In addition to "Auntie Maria" I'm free-lancing full time because I'm not even *writing* "Auntie Maria" any more. I'm just digging out the back shows from eight and nine years ago, telling my girl to type them up fresh, and sending them in. So far no complaints, and $20,000 a year without even going to the trouble of doing the work. I'm staggering under monetary commitments. Nobody the wiser. People are so damn stupid it's unbelievable. In my opinion, one of the best things that could ever happen was somebody come along and drop the atom bomb on them and get it over with.

Back to the salt mines.

With personal felicitations,

[*to Abner Klang, New York, telegram*]

APPRECIATE YOUR SENDING ME SOONEST COLLECT THE NAME AND ADDRESS OF THE AGENCY WHICH HANDLES THE AUNTIE MARIA RADIO SHOW.

LEE

[*to his brother, Ogden, Utah*]

October 16

My dear old Dee,

The hand on the envelope said "Dee Youngdahl," and the script was familiar, but for a moment I could not put the two together, and I said to Beth, "Oh God, there's been a death, or somebody's terribly sick," and she said, "Well, let's find out the worst," and so we opened it, and I have walked on air all day, and thought of nothing else but this rarest of events—a letter from you.

But now let me tell you what a strange and unbelievable and remarkable coincidence it is, because (you won't believe this, and I wouldn't expect anybody *to* believe it if I didn't have the facts to back it up) just as the mailman was coming up the street, *just as I was standing there,* I had *in my hand* a letter I wrote last night to Garafolo. Who was the subject of that letter?

You, Sir, you.

What did I say? Well, let me keep you in suspense a little bit. I am a natural story-teller and cannot bear to give the headline first, just as Alexander Irwin is a natural boxer, just as you are a natural farmer, and every good man plays his role, and no role is more important than any other role, and nobody is better than anybody else. As Mom said to me in a letter only yesterday, "there are differences in people," and of course she is proud of me, and Dad is proud of me, just as they are proud of you. All her letters shine with pride for you. Well, of course—you know that as well as I do, so I don't know why I'm wasting my breath laboring the obvious.

Anyhow, Garafolo looking fine, and Alexander Irwin looking fine and without a mark on him, swept up to the house yesterday morning in a glistening airport cab. I switched on my tape-recorder.

ME: Irwin, what shall I call you, Alexander Irwin or what?

GARAFOLO: He don't care what you call him. You don't care what he calls you.

IRWIN: No.

ME: I'll call him Irwin. How's that? Irwin, you look fit. Feeling fine, are you? Ready to take on Sanzobo?

GARAFOLO: He'll be ready at the bell rings.

ME: You're not a talkative fellow, are you?

IRWIN: No, I not talkive.

GARAFOLO: Let's talk, no machine.

BETH (coffee cups clattering): Yes, Lee, turn it off, darling.

GARAFOLO: Yes.

ME: . . . a record of our remarks.

GARAFOLO: Why not forget it and speak about . . .

ME: Are you tired? Would you care to take a nap? We have plenty of beds.

GARAFOLO: Lee has a whole flock of children, ain't you, Lee? How many children you have?

IRWIN: Is that right?

ME: Do you sleep pretty well?

IRWIN: I sleep OK. I get sideways I sleep.

ME: Do you like to sleep?

IRWIN: Not partickly.

ME: What do you like to do? What are your enthusiasms, your spare-time pursuits? Look at it this way, what is it that you do that if—if you didn't do it—this isn't much of a sentence—what do you do that if you didn't do you'd feel your day was incomplete?

IRWIN: Punch the bag maybe. Mr. Gafo . . .

GARAFOLO: Not talking, Lee, that's one thing he don't . . .

ME: Do you like to fight? Do you love fighting? . . . Well, do you love money? . . . Why? Why do you want money? Do you fight for money? Is money why you fight?

IRWIN: I likes money.

ME: Why? For what purpose? Is there something money can buy that you don't now have that you want to have that you can't have without money? Is that why you . . .

GARAFOLO: Money can buy nothing but happiness.

IRWIN: Money build my count in the bank.

ME: What bank?

IRWIN: My home bank.

ME: Where's that?

IRWIN: Mobile. Mr. Gafo . . .

ME: What's your favorite city? Now you've traveled around a bit and seen some cities, now San Francisco, queen of them all, although my favorite city is actually Ogden—where my brother lives—where the streets are regular and rectangular, and life is regular, too. But San Francisco! When Billy Graham was here he said, "I never preach a sermon on Heaven here because people might think I'm talking about the Bay Area." There were 38,000 saints in Seals Stadium, and me, largest crowd the park ever had. I love New York, too, if only for its wickedness, and Boston. Boston leaves you alone. Chicago fevers you. In St. Louis I get the heart-breaking feeling I'm drowning in nostalgia—why, it's almost like being in Charleston or New Orleans. Phoenix is a lady in shorts. I hate Los Angeles, but only out of loyalty to San Francisco. In fact, don't tell anybody but I've had some good times in Los Angeles. In Seattle you're always waiting for your ship to come in. Minneapolis has brains. But you know, I've never been to Cincinnati. Damn it, I don't know *what* my favorite city is outside of here and Ogden, but every man must have one. What's *your* favorite city?

IRWIN: Mobile.

ME: I notice you come out fairly slow with the bell, but with great interest. I believe you love fighting—getting out there, the roar of the crowd, and you and only you, and Cottrell the other night. Doesn't fighting represent something to you—some sort of a problem to be solved?

IRWIN: When the man standing up is my problem.

GARAFOLO: If the machine was off we could discuss . . .

IRWIN: When the man laying down my problem all solve.

ME: When you fight are you angry at your opponent? . . . You know, as Garafolo may have told you, I was an extremely successful fighter, and you know what I think? I think you can be hit over your left hand.

IRWIN: Mr. Gafo.

GARAFOLO: What makes him angry is talking, Lee. Don't talking make you angry, Irwin?

IRWIN: That's right, like talking in some machine particklly.

BETH: Yes, darling, let's turn it off . . .

Now, *that's* what I call a natural boxer, whose day isn't done until he's punched the bag, like your day isn't done—and I can see you now—until you've gone out and walked your fences, because you are the natural man who feeds us city folk: from you our meat, from you the salt to salt it with.

We drove around town a little, ate a big spaghetti meal at DiMaggio's, and Garafolo presented his problem, which is simply this: he needs a little money to carry him through Irwin's shaping for Sanzobo, to pay off a few accumulated past expenses (took a financial loss on the Los Angeles fight for the sake of the chance against Cottrell), and to pay the show-up guarantee in New York. The amount wasn't much, but Beth and I said we'd talk it over in private and whip him off a letter within 24 hours to Peekskill. In return for the small amount, he'd give me a 12½% interest in Irwin. What an opportunity! Win or lose I'd get more than my money back after the Sanzobo fight, and all the future is gravy. I expect that a one-eighth share of Irwin ought to be worth, in time to come, anywhere up to a million dollars, and to think that I could buy it for a small amount, just because I happened to be lying in Garafolo's path in his moment of financial stress, makes me wonder why us Youngdahls have all the luck.

Coming back from the airport, Beth said, "It's a risk, but so is everything else."

"I don't like it," I said, "and I'll tell you why. Because, to me, Garafolo means more than just Garafolo. I associate *Dee* with Garafolo, the three of us, we were partners together."

"A team's a team," she said, "and that's a fact. You can't take a team that was three, and drop Dee out, and still call it a team any more."

"All right," I said, "I'll write Garafolo No."

"Not at all," she said. (I want you to see how the big idea was Beth's idea. I want to keep the record straight and give credit where credit is due.) "Just tell him he must cut Dee in *too*."

"Dee wouldn't happen to have the cash," I said. "After all, while I've been free to roam around and save up a penny or two, Dee's stayed home and assumed the whole responsibility of the farm."

"Very simple," said Beth. "We'll put up the cash, and Dee can draw on his share after we get our share back. Let's not do any favors for Dee."

This appeared to be a splendid plan, and unless you have some objection you now own one-sixteenth of Irwin. Take it or leave it. If I don't hear from you I'll assume you're agreeable. A team's a team and that's that, and we are partners again, as once we were.

Your loving brother,

P.S. Don't breathe a word until plans are final, but I think I may be coming through Ogden pretty soon, and bringing the gang with me.

P.P.S. What are you and I ever going to do about The Great Chiffonier Crisis?

Wednesday, October 17

[*from Elvin R. Outerbridge, San Francisco*]

DEPARTMENT OF ENGLISH

To: Youngdahl
From: Outerbridge
Date:
Subject:

In June I shall teach my last hour and return to the neighborhood of Ogden for a period of reflexion upon the labyrinth of these years. There have been mysteries, but few so charming as the latest. I am first impelled to feel privileged to be included among those whom you honor with a joke. You do not joke except with your equals, as you would not strike a smaller man. You think to joke with me by attaching a sweet old bishop to my diminishing time.

Yet I now wonder if it is not some deeper reason you think it imperative to declare to me a churchly intention, some imagined turn of your own you serve. If you thought to move the bishop, even while you deceived him, you have succeeded —his eyes were tears, the hundredth sheep was in his arms. As for me, however, the idea of privilege surrendered to another, and I have come to think your comic behavior accountable to some jitters.

Do not permit your imagination to project upon other people jealousies you would feel if you were they. Beware of the pride which holds that all men wish they were you. (I illustrate by citing the tale told of Sam Johnson: Said a lady to him: "Sir, your penis is sticking out." Said Johnson in reply: "Madame, do not flatter yourself: it is *hanging* out.")

You have a most engaging way with people. Your laughter produces laughter, and gives our Coffee Bar a tone whose bracing qualities prevent our minds from stiffening with our joints. For that we cherish you, and for your remarkable success in rousing and therefore teaching students whom most of us but faintly stir, though we were teaching when you were sucking. As if by some magic sensitivity of ear, you receive from all with whom you deal their theme, their principal echoing chord, and, like some great mimic of the Garrick school, you play it back to them, and they, hearing you play, hearing that you hear, play louder and louder and louder, and reveal to you their essence. To only a few, perhaps only to those of us who may once have been you, do you reveal yourself.

You tease, you evoke, draw out, cajole. You have a timing about you which I speculate may have been trained in you by games: you might sometime advise some bright young student, casting about for a topic for a dissertation, to question whether men who, as boys, played the rough-and-tumble playground games, do not in after life better succeed than bookish boys, by reason of a better timing.

The fact remains, however, that you do not know me, although I know you. Every fighter must sometime lose a match. You will know me better as you grow stronger. Even this moment you suddenly know me better; I therefore need say no more, except to wish you the thirty years which have been granted to me, and to tell you, as you step into my decades, that they will be, for you, largely happy. The profession keeps a man young—more, I think, than any other. Every autumn, with the return of new young, one freshly knows that time passes but that life, in its essential form, repeats with the seasons. Thus you will be required to write, I fear, thirty years hence, a memorandum exactly like this to a boy still under forty in his jitters.

Please remember me to your fine father.

[*from Abner Klang, New York, special delivery*]

October 16 Lee I wing this to you special because I just got o the line with Enright. He says you positively cannot go orward with a San rancisco production and that is the answer as I expected. I am unhappy about this because Purdy is involved.

I want to stay on a riendly ooting with Purdy so you break the news to him without getting him mad but only orcing him to see matters in the light o practical common sense. Tell yoursel the truth. Can a show out there net you more than $80 or $90 a per ormance calculating two shows a week which you can roll up in a ball and throw spitballs at the students with compared to the author o Bonanza Boat which is Enright's show sitting around drawing $5200 a week while the author o amily Place is earning $2800 a week and isn't even a musical. Purdy himsel or his own little show drew $1200 a week prior to closing. Idea. Maybe Purdy doesn't want you to move up in the money bracket with him. Think about that awhile. Don't say I said so.

Your own interests only at heart sometimes you act like you don't want to do business on the streets where the money is. Don't be ambivalent. Sometimes I have the crazy eeling that while I am working my heart out or you you are sitting back there praying or me to ail. I know this can't be true. I I had an eraser I'd erase it.

Whizzer also sent me the he O U signed which brings up another delicate subject. You have about as much chance o getting back $450 rom Whizzer as swimming the Atlantic or any comparable Ocean holding your breath ighting wild sharks with one hand and pushing the Queen Mary in ront. I got him two picture jobs and he did one and hal o the other until due to some minor irritation started around the lot beating up everybody including stenographers and scrubwomen which was no way to act. Whizzer is through. However there is a little money that dri ts in his account here and there and now and then so I'll just book it in your name and pay you back like that. There is nothing illegal in it. The Government does the same and his wi e is another so you might as well stand in line with all the rest.

I had many con erences with Window 9 and the credit situation is now clari ied as ollows.

IRST LASH—The Hard Puncher. Based on the novel by Lee Youngdahl

SECOND LASH—Victor Wenk

How many million dollars would it cost you to write that little speech or the re eree or Wenk instead o sending him religious ravings.

Gabriella Bodeen walked out on the cast so you can thank your riend or doing you such a nice little avor since while the present girl has a bigger bust than the state of Texas and the Gul o Mexico combined she is unknown whereas Bodeen would shoot the viewing up on a hard night when Window 9 bucks or its li e against the prize ights. So she cost you a million viewers while out o the million one was a producer who might have bought it or stage or pictures but instead will switch in on the prize ights. You have the loveliest riends. Don't tell her I said so. Don't tell Purdy what I said.

A business man drops in or his weekly pickup at his psychiatrist. The psychiatrist says I am sick and tired hearing your insane paradichlorochodomies so just talk into my tape recorder while I go down to Ye Old Corner Bar or a drink. He goes down. Pretty soon he is sitting at the bar with a woman who is beauti ul or no joke but you can orget about the woman when along comes his patient and also sits down. I thought I told you to stay up there and talk into my tape recorder. Well replies the patient I got to thinking during the week o many ideas I was a raid I would orget so I talked in my own tape recorder during the week and now my tape recorder is upstairs talking into your tape recorder.

Ever yours,

[from Abner Klang, New York, telegram]

AUNTIEMARIA AGENCIED BENWINDER MINTER 501 MADISON AVENUE. WHAT'S UP?

ABNER

[*to Abner Klang, New York, special delivery*]

October 17

Dear Abner,

Because you failed to catch up with that fly ball you cost us the World Series. You have one more big chance. You're on the two-yard line, the clock is running out, the ball is under your arm. If you carry it over, you've won the game and the girl and the big job at Alumni's wholesale warehouse, but if you don't carry it over you've lost the game and the girl and your job.

Signals! Exhume from your chaotic premises my letter to you of October 8. Carry it to Window 9. Insist upon the terms therein.

Nothing else will do. Don't you see the chicanery, the villainy, the outright misrepresentation they are perpetrating with their word "by"? To what does it refer? They are attempting to deceive an innocent public into believing that the television show is "by" me.

Then stands Victor Wenk's name—alone. Who is he? Millions will ask. Is he producer? Is he director? Is he the author of the commercial announcements? Is he an actor? Is he a cameraman? Is he the doorman, or perhaps the Window-washer himself? Maybe he is the product sponsored, a Victor Wenk, like a Victor Record?

You had better go over. You have nothing to lose but Lee Youngdahl.

No, I don't suppose, to a man who happily skates along on a 25-letter alphabet, nor who, for fifteen years, has abstained from most forms of punctuation, a little word like "by" means much. But, Sir, you are incorrect: it is all. It is my life. Now, whose life shall it be, yours or mine? Save me and save yourself.

In unspeakable fury,

[*to Harold Rosenblatt, New Haven, Conn.,*]
special delivery]

October 17

Dear Harold,

Let me be the first, even when the word is sad.

Mr. Outerbridge is dead. I do not know details, except that it occurred in sleep, either late last night or early in the morning hours today. You may wish to drop a line to Mrs. Outerbridge. He was to have retired in June.

Death quickens us with love for living friends, as I for you, and so send Sylvia and you and yours from Beth and me and mine a wish for life. Be not grave. Remember how saith Sam the old pro Johnson: "My boys, let us be grave: here comes a fool."

[to Louis Garafolo, Kurman's Camp,
Peekskill, New York]

October 17

Dear Garafolo,

May I just ask that you amend our contract of the other day in the following way: instead of my now possessing a 12½% share in Irwin, please reduce my share to 6¼%, assigning the other 6¼% to: Mr. Dee Youngdahl, R. F. D. South, Ogden, Utah.

I am sure this will be easy enough to do merely by including my name with Dee's in the contract, and then you may cause an additional copy of the contract to be prepared for him, and sent to him at the above address. After the return to me of my $3,000 all returns above that amount shall be equally divided between Dee and me. If there is anything unclear about this please tell me, but I don't think your lawyer should have any difficulty in understanding it.

I hope you had a good trip. I watched the papers to see if any planes went down, but since none did I assume your safety.

My plans are now quite definite. I leave here on the 25th via Ogden on an important business trip to New York. Don't forget to see my TV show on the night of the 26th. I will expect that you, instead of watching mere fights in the TV flesh, will want to watch *The Hard Puncher* for a view of fighting as it touches upon the soul. I will be watching in Ogden, surrounded by all the sturdy burghers, flying out of there that night for the island of Manhattan near the City of Peekskill. See you there.

Always and always your boy,

Thursday, October 18

[to Abner Klang, New York]

October 18

Dear Abner,

By now you have my special-delivery letter of yesterday and have been activated into useful forms of behavior. Herewith I swiftly proceed to two other points in your letter of the 16th.

First, you ask me to withdraw the play from Paul Purdy at University Theater. This I have not the least intention of doing for you or for Enright or for anyone else. I may be ambivalent, but I'm not *that* ambivalent.

Second, I will tell you a little anecdote relevant to the Whizzer matter. Once there was a Scotchman from Scotland who formed a friendship with an Englishman from England. Their names were, respectively, J. Boswell, and S. Johnson. Sometimes it happened that S. Johnson did not wish to be interrupted by callers; yet he would never permit a servant to "deny" him—*i. e.,* to say that he was not at home when he was. One day J. Boswell asked S. Johnson why he did not permit himself to be denied, whereupon S. Johnson replied that if he were to teach his servants to lie *for* him they should soon conceive the plan of lying *against* him. Therefore allow me to hear no more of one man's money drifting over into another man's account.

In short, don't think. Act! But, of course, don't act until I tell you how. Remain my puppet and you'll soon have puppets of your own.

Things are in a terrible state of confusion here. It appears that I am called upon to solve all the problems of the University before my departure next week. Anybody but me wouldn't stand a chance.

October 18

Mr. Benwinder and Mr. Minter Associates
501 Madison Avenue
New York, New York

Dear Mr. Benwinder and Mr. Minter,

I hesitated writing this letter to you because I am afraid you will laugh at my writing, but the man at the radio station said I should write you all the same, and you would not laugh, and I am.

A terrible thing happened to Auntie Maria who I have listened to every day since she began so many years and years ago. You have made a terrible mistake. You are sending out over the air waves the very same events which happened eight years ago.

You see, every day I write in my little book, which I keep in our old family chiffanear, which came west with us when we came here with our dear departed now, just exactly what happened, and I can tell you the very same things are happening over again.

That is pure carelessness. I am a buyer of all the things Auntie Maria tells us we ought to buy and use, but now I am beginning to wonder if such pure carelessness on Auntie Maria's part ever gets into the things she says I ought to buy and use, and does she know. Somebody must tell her to stop that pure carelessness.

I have talked about this to a number of the other girls and they are beginning to get the same idea. One of them was so angry she said she could cry at the way people are treating us, like we were "dopes" and she is going to stop buying the things Auntie Maria says until the conditions improve. My best wishes to Auntie Maria and Dr. George and Susannah and especially the twins. My sister has twins.

Yours very truthfully,
Mrs. Y. Dahl
18 Diamond Street
San Francisco 14
California

Friday, October 19

[from Tremont C. Katt, Katt's Air College, Monterey, California, postcard]

Thursday

I see by Herb Caen's column that you are flying to New York. Did you ever think about *gliding* to New York? Lotsa publicity. I will get the sponsors and you will get the glory. Tell me in a hurry. You and I in the silent air. It appeals.

Tom

[*to Paul Purdy*]

DEPARTMENT OF ENGLISH

To: Purdy
From: Youngdahl
Date: [Friday, October 19]
Subject:

My decision of this morning is final and unalterable. I am sorry for the inconvenience it will cause you, but that is the way things are. Please return the manuscript to me at your convenience.

[*to Gabriella Bodeen, New York*]

October 19

My dearest Gabriella,

There was a man in the land of San Francisco, whose name was Youngdahl, and that man was perfect and upright, and one that feared God and eschewed evil.

And there were born unto him sons and daughters, and his substance also was car and job and prospects and a very great household.

Now there was a day when the sons of God came to present themselves before the LORD, and Satan came also among them.

And the LORD said unto Satan, Whence comest thou? Then Satan answered the LORD and said, From going to and fro in San Francisco, and walking up and down the steep hills in it.

And the LORD said unto Satan, Hast thou considered my servant Youngdahl? for there is none like him in the earth, a perfect and an upright man, and one that feareth God and escheweth evil.

So Satan went forth from the Lord and smote Youngdahl with Theater Arts magazine, and his wife who was Beth saw therein a photograph of Gabriella, and was wroth.

So was Youngdahl sore afflicted, for vexation killeth the foolish man, and jealousy slayeth his wife, and the roar of the lioness is scattered abroad.

Again there was a day when the sons of God came to present themselves before the Lord, and Satan came also among them to present himself before the Lord.

And the Lord said unto Satan, From whence comest thou? And Satan answered the Lord and said, From sore afflicting your servant Youngdahl, a perfect and an upright man.

I showed him in Theater Arts a photograph in the color of the rainbow, and it was a symbol of Gabriella, and she was perfect and at ease, and not upright.

Then spoke Satan and said, Also have I delivered him to the ungodly, and made him unhappy among his fellows, and cast him into the hand of Tenure.

He was at peace and I brake him asunder, taken him by the neck and dashed him into two, confused him with twin desires, and his face is foul with weeping.

I have set him up for my mark, and

compassed him with archers roundabout. I cleaveth his reins asunder, and I poureth out his gall upon the ground.

And Youngdahl spoke, saying, Now my soul is scourged out within me, and I am become like dust and ashes. Out of the chamber of the West cometh my storm.

My breath kindleth coals, and a flame goeth forth from my mouth. In my neck abideth strength. The flakes of my flesh are joined together.

I shall wander to my brother, whose house is in the wilderness, and the salt land is his dwelling place. He scorneth the tumult of the city.

This shall be at the end of next week. Neither heareth my brother the shout of the driver. The range of the mountains is his pasture. He searcheth after every green thing.

And I shall wander after to Manhattan, for men here clap their hands at me, and hiss me out of this place, and the topaz of Bartholomew Enright is in New York.

Costly my raiment. In it will I make many supplications to thee? Will I make a covenant with thee? Or wilt thou play with me as with a bird?

My heart is as firm as a stone; yea, firm as the nether millstone. Behold, my belly is as wine which hath no vent; like new bottles it is ready to burst.

Yet shall I be again as in the ripeness of my days. Lay up these words in thy heart.

Then was Satan pleased and saw how Youngdahl's step turned out of the way, how his heart walked after his eye, and his foot hasted to deceit. And Satan spoke in the east to Gabriella, saying, If thou darest write to him you had best do so @ his University, lest his wife grind greater than a thousand tempests, and rent your mantle, and fall upon you, and smite you, and shave your head, and afflict you with boils from the sole of your foot to your crown, and great shall be your grief, and she shall plague you gaunt with want and famine, and drive you forth out of the land, and calamity shall she visit upon you to your full age.

Lo, here is my signature.

[*enclosure to Gabriella Bodeen*]

ARE WE DRAGGING MEN TO HELL BY OUR MODERN DRESS?

CRIMES OF PASSION DISHONORED LIVES IMMORALITY

A GOOD LADY SAID, "These knee length dresses are not modest. The Holy Spirit showed me that at least half of the calf of the leg should be covered. Some feel all the calf of the leg should be covered."

Low necks, short dresses scarcely to the knees, bare arms, painted faces—in a word—everything to arouse passion and lust is the order of the day. "Everybody does it!" I know—but do you belong to the "everybodies" or are you a pilgrim?

In a neighboring town lives a boy who was graduated from the State University with the highest honors. Later he had a fine position but acquired a venereal disease, went insane, and is now in the insane asylum part of the time. I went to Bible school, and one day the teacher had a special meeting of the girls and told them if they would let the Lord talk to them, they would lengthen their dresses. When the school had a social gathering, one boy left the party when the girls were playing games, etc. He could see too much, he said.

(ED. NOTE. Rolled stockings and similar styles have a direct bearing on crime incitation.)

When women come here with knee length dresses and stoop to pick up apples, I think the men can see more than the Lord intended them to see. I would rather wear my dresses a longer length and please the Lord than try to please a hard-to-please fickle world. We surely will never send men to Hell by wearing longer dresses.

John Wesley said gay and costly apparel tends to influence lust. During the first hundred years of her ministry, Methodism was the greatest power for righteousness of any movement since Pentecost. In those days of her glory, Methodism always insisted on plainness of attire.

What does Charles Finney (one of the greatest God-used evangelists of all time) say? "I will confess that I was formerly myself in error. I believed that the best way for Christians to pursue was to dress so as not to be noticed, to follow the fashions so as not to be noticed, to follow the fashions so as not to appear singular. But I have seen my error and now wonder greatly at my former blindness."

I am trusting the Lord to keep my three sons pure. Can the Lord protect young people? I know He can, because He has kept me moral. I couldn't commit adultery if you would give me the whole world; neither can I get mixed up in an affair with some other woman's husband.

(ED. NOTE. Adultery is common these days.)

If He can keep me moral, He can keep your son and daughter moral. The power of the Devil is great, but praise God, the Lord has more power. I don't want Jesus to say to me some day, "By the exposure of your flesh you have dragged men to Hell." Do you?

—*Mrs. Dewitt Smith*

(PILGRIM TRACT SOCIETY, *Randleman, N. C.* Supported by voluntary gifts of its readers. Tracts free as the Lord supplies the funds. Send postage for 100 samples of tracts.)

[*to Harold Rosenblatt, New Haven, Conn., telegram*]

PLEASE TELEPHONE PAUL AND TELL HIM I FORGIVE HIM EVERYTHING AND HE MAY HAVE THE PLAY BACK AGAIN. HE WILL UNDERSTAND. THIS IS URGENT. I WILL PAY. LETTER FOLLOWS. INCIDENTALLY I HAVE RESIGNED EFFECTIVE JUNE TO ACCEPT AT HARVARD FOR THE FALL.

LEE

Saturday, October 20

[from Clinton W. Blalock, Harvard University]

October 18

My dear Youngdahl,

Your charming letter and your equally charming credentials are here. Your *vita* we have passed from hand to hand. A more relaxed, gay, and informal presentation we have not seen in a long time. We are in the process of revising it along more suitable lines, and I should be mightily surprised (although I am not over-much given to optimism) if you do not soon receive an official and irresistible offer. California's loss shall be Harvard's gain.

I wonder if your "salary expected" might not be reduced to—let us say—$9,500. Possibly you arrived at your own figure in terms of California standards; in any case, it is inconsistent with the prevailing scale.

Simonsen and I and others will meet with you October 30 in New York. This was accomplished with a call to your agent, who proves to be the model of your accurate advertisement. He asked me whether I had business with you, or whether I wished merely talk; if the former, he said, it might be done through him; if the latter, he could see no point to it. He asked me if we would be traveling on a Harvard expense account, whether it was small or ample, and when I told him ample his respect for Harvard University noticeably quickened. Did we at Harvard, he asked, publish magazines? What are our rates to authors? Are any of our stories ever bought for filming in Hollywood or for adaptation to the Broadway stage? What was my own field? When I replied "The Eighteenth Century" he directed me to "name some people in that century." He asked me were the queens of that century salacious, to which I replied, "Indeed," whereupon he directed me to write a novel, without delay, of five hundred pages or more about the wickedest, sexiest queen of the century, or, if she were not wicked enough, I should combine the wickednesses of several into one, rush the result to him, and we should soon be millionaires. He commanded me, however, not to include Johnson and Boswell in my work, since you have "wrapped them up."

The conclusion to your boxing career, regrettable in itself, was all the more so in that you were conquered in Boston. Let us hope the event has not prejudiced you against this place. Please consider revising your figure for "salary expected," and please know how very much I look forward to our meeting.

Yours most sincerely,

[*from Whizzer Harlow, Santa Fé, New Mexico*]

October 18

Friend Lee,

I am bashed in the mouth. Consider it done. You are right, right, right, you bashed me, you sat me down on the seat of my seat, and I cleared my cabin and my life of my little Spanish girl who retreated with pleading eyes, and I machined two stories I wrote by hand in Dallas, and whipped them to Abner, and a third is in the process, and a fourth and a fifth are in my head. I thank you, I thank you, and when you see me you shall see a man whose debts are paid and shoes are soled and the seat of his seat an honorable shine.

But in New York you shall not see me, nor anywhere awhile, and your own clickety clickety is next to nothing next to mine. Now travel I, now flow, yet move the body not, and the fire roars but the wine stays corked, and Hector with smug demeanor patrols his acreage, but I see him not, nor wave, nor pause for speech. He who provides merely the means is commonplace, but devotion and industry come rare to a cabin, and she spills, she moves, she flies, dances, twinkles, and I her master, and bash me any time, it is my tonic, and I have drunk well and deep.

More sometime,

[to Harold Rosenblatt, New Haven, Conn.]

October 20

Dear Harold,

I have resigned, effective June, to accept at Harvard in the Fall. At the insistence of a vast and enthusiastic delegation of Harvard Youngdahlites, I leave here next Thursday to meet with them in New York, where we will close the matter. I suppose that you will miss me, although your silence gives me no firm reason to believe that this is the case.

I thank you for phoning Paul Purdy, who has dried his eyes and resumed casting, and now I suppose I owe it to you to tell you why you phoned him. At a sacrifice measurable in terms of the emotional cost of my having given away two perfectly good football tickets I hereby do so. The day of the game is bright and clear, as in the books my Lucien reads, the sun shines on your house, the whistle blows the kickoff, and the drama begins.

Since, when I came home from school Wednesday, Beth said nothing to me of Mr. Outerbridge, I concluded she had not heard, and therefore—so fond am I of the dramatic, as opposed to the merely communicative—I presented the news to her in a manner most unique: taking from the shelf *Job: A Disquisition,* I wrote upon the flyleaf, "The author of this book dined with us October 6, and, eleven days thereafter, expired." I held the page before Beth, who was grating carrots at the sink, and she, with poise magnificent, without pause nor cease of motion, commented, "Jesus, Lee, that's a *terrible* way of telling somebody something."

We attempted to compose a note to Mrs. Outerbridge in which we should avoid the clichés common to the occasion but at length, despairing, we shifted our tactics and composed one which is but a single cliché, or series of linked clichés.

We turned then to the serious business of adjusting the fates of the living to the light of the new alignment. Triumph followed triumph. I phoned Mrs. Rudy, who is the reigning power on the Committee on Committees, and asked her who would replace Mr. Outerbridge on my Tenure Committee. She pretended to have given the matter no thought. "How about Red Traphagen?" she said.

"The failure of his summer," I said, "might work against me. No." Bitterness in Red turns to whimsy, and he might take the whimsical notion to see how I'd react to destitution.

"Posh," said Mrs. Rudy. "You just go ahead, then, and tell Paul Purdy just go ahead and pick somebody," a proposal whose convenience elated me, and I phoned Paul and told him I wanted someone weak, another craven Clinch, some slave whom he might intimidate, and rescue me from the hungry streets, and I went happily to bed, and visions of Tenure danced in my head.

Definitely For Me	*Definitely Against Me*
Paul Purdy	Mr. Gamble
Clinch (brainwashed by Paul)	Harbidge
Human X (Purdy's intimidated slave)	

Yesterday morning, a new and double victory! Mr. Gamble summoned me to his office and asked me whether I felt competent to replace Mr. Outerbridge in The Testament As Literature. In exchange, I should be relieved of my one remaining freshman class. "I feel competent," I said, "to teach anything written in the English language. I was teethed upon the Testament. The Bible was our bible. I am luxuriously at home everywhere between creation and resurrection and in and out of flood and pestilence. Sometimes I feel that God and I practically *collaborated* on that book."

He accepted this as an expression of confidence, and he next informed me that I might inform the Committee on Freshman Staff, of which, in your absence, I am Chairman *pro tem,* that he—Mr. Gamble—sought quick approval of a young man from Princeton who would be (said Mr. Gamble) a strong addition to our ranks.

This I angrily protested. I had studied the credentials of the young man from Princeton. His application was very neat and legible. His photograph was of a clean-cut young man who spends not less than thirty minutes before his morning mirror. He had been a member of the very best Princeton eating society, and he had then gone ahead at Harvard to produce very neat, clean-cut, legible, well-dressed academic papers in which (I am sure) he has always been cautious to avoid saying anything that has not been frequently and respectably said before.

My own preference among the candidates was for one W. Wycherly Wood, born in Elyria, Ohio, and a graduate of Nebraska, whose hair, according to his photograph, stands straight on end, and who is not above a pun, even if it may cost him a job.

> I conceive of the clashroom [wrote Wood] as a place you go into not so much to describe the past as to knock everybody's head against your own so that by a study of the past we might better understand today and tomorrow. I conceive [he added] of democracy as more important than knowledge or literature. What I mean is, only in a democratic atmosphere can true investigation take place. But we cannot have a democratic give-and-take between teacher and students if the teacher is a commissar: he must behave himself as if he believes himself truly in partnership with his students in their common endeavor to uncover the probable facts leading to more or less reasonable conclusions. Until the teacher freely confesses, in the classroom *act,* his own fundamental inadequacy, he is lying to himself and to his students. My problem is that everywhere I have been in this education

circus I find almost everybody lying to protect himself from his students and his colleagues, everybody afraid of saying, "I don't know." Therefore I have been in bitter conflict everywhere.

People tell me I will grow mellower, but I am twenty-four with no signs of mellowness setting in . . .

"A rather blunt boy," said Mr. Gamble.

"You want a teacher," I said, "or you want table manners?"

"What's he hiding," Mr. Gamble asked, "behind that *W*?"

"I'll get him to face up to plain old Will Wood," I said.

"Your Will be done," said Mr. Gamble.

"My Will Wood be done," I said, and I was joyous, and I strode out with a gay step because I love to win and hate to lose. I am most aggressive. Then, at The Coffee Bar, I encountered Paul, and all turned to dust and ashes.

"Who'd you put on my Tenure Committee?" I said.

"Whoyoucallit," he said.

"Who's whoyoucallit?" I said.

"Cecile," he said.

I did not strike him. I did not swear at him. I did not raise my voice. I simply told him that, upon the instant, my play was to be withdrawn from University Theater, and that I hoped we might, during the remainder of my year here, avoid every association. I left my coffee untouched, rose, and departed. The new state of affairs in that moment may best be illustrated by reference to the accompanying table:

Definitely For Me	*Definitely Against Me*
Mr. Outerbridge (deceased)	Mr. Gamble
	Harbidge
	Paul Purdy
	Clinch (merrily, in Paul's wake)
	Cecile

That night, her sympathy-begetting belly protruding, Willa came to the house to tell us that Paul, after our interview, quivering with chagrin, arrived home, went to bed, wept, would not eat, and would tell her only that somehow he had terribly misjudged me. His delicacy was touching, and it softened me somewhat toward him. Of course, with Beth present, I could not introduce the question of Cecile, but I told Willa to go home and tell Paul he could now stop crying and start eating. "I retract everything," I said, "and as a matter of fact I've just wired Harold to phone Paul and tell him so." Then, of course, I wired you. You obliged, and I thank you. Paul will have a deeper sense hereafter of the mystery of me, and so will you.

"I have the most singular mind was ever formed." Certainly it is circuitous. The idea of wiring New Haven as a means of transmitting a message across Twin Peaks amuses me no end, especially in view of the fact that the message had already been delivered. It will also amuse my biographers, although it puzzles Beth. "It is because you are idle," she says, "and because, I suppose, whatever it is it makes Youngdahl what Youngdahl is."

Did you receive my play? Shall we write a Journal to each other? Will you see me in New York? Have you found out for me what the two blue beans are doing in the blue bladder, and why they are blue? Did I tell you that your house is rotting away?

Now I shall write my little letter of resignation to Mr. Gamble. Tell Sylvia that Beth will miss her, and she will miss Beth. Yet you and I might correspond so long as the mail flies, even as we do now, don't we?

Farewell, etc.,

Sunday, October 21

October 20

Mr. Victor Wenk
Window 9
New York

Dear Mr. Wenk:

I have your special-delivery letter of October 11.

Hard Puncher and Irishman come out of corner, presumably for instructions, "at bell."

What bell? Is there a fire? Is it time for church? Is school out? Did it ever occur to you to go watch a prize-fight and attempt to link for yourself the pattern of bells to action?

Referee tells them that if anybody is knocked down he must be up by the count of ten.

Why? Don't they know? Do you mean to tell me they are professional boxers and they *don't know?* Impossible. I can't believe it, and nobody else will believe it either. My mother knows it. Every child in the nation knows it.

Hard Puncher says, "Let's start the fight and not waste any more time."

Why? In the novel he says "Let's start." Everybody knows what is to be started, and why he wants to start it. That's why they're there—to fight. They're not there to play chess, or they wouldn't be wearing boxing gloves. If they were there to dance they would be dressed more formally, and they would have girls with them. If they were there to race motorboats they would have motorboats with them, and they would be nearer the water. They are not there to jump out of airplanes in parachutes or they would have parachutes with them. Do not use more words than your characters need. Allow your characters to talk only to each other, not to some un-named, unknown, invisible, imaginary, remote, and abstract "viewer." This "viewer," for all you know, is smarter than you are.

In Utah we say, "Actions speak louder than words." This is the principle of drama. Not to believe in this principle is to show contempt for the human mind. Contempt for the human mind is Communistic and Fascistic, where the words contradict the action. Communism and Fascism are un-American. So straighten up.

I am sorry Bodeen quit the cast, but I don't blame her. I would have quit the cast myself.

Cordially,

Monday, October 22

[from Harold Rosenblatt, New Haven, Conn.]

October 19

Dear Lee,

I am mildly curious to know the meaning of the telephone call I have just made to Paul.

Do you really own 12½% of a prizefighter? I own 60% of a house. Houses last longer.

Sylvia and I send our love to Beth and to the children and, I suppose, to you.

[*to Mrs. Elvin Outerbridge, San Francisco*]

October 22

Dear Mrs. Outerbridge,

Your husband's passing fills Beth and me with a regret inexpressible. He was loved by all who knew him. He was wise, generous, and just, a scholar and a gentleman.

Yours most sincerely,

Tuesday, October 23

[to his mother, Ogden, Utah]

October 23

Dear Mom,

I send to you the item concerning Mr. Outerbridge's death, from the school paper. You say in a letter, "We wonder who remembers us," and you may be sure Mr. Outerbridge remembered you, for on the day he died I received a memorandum from him pertaining to school matters, concluding with the words, "Please remember me to your fine father and your fine mother." Also, he had nicely smoothed out matters between me and Bishop Veenstra.

But now, here's a great surprise for you. I leave here with everybody but Beth and Tetsey for Ogden Thursday night, arriving Friday morning, remaining until after the TV show, and then slipping away by air on an urgent business trip to New York. The kids will stay with you. I'll be back in Ogden from my New-York trip in time for Thanksgiving. What do you think of that for a surprise?

I'll be bringing Red Traphagen's autograph for Bobby and Giff, although why they should want Red and not me I don't know. I was a better boxer than Red was a baseball player, as I frequently tell him.

Did Red Traphagen ever write a book which was made into a TV show? I think not. Do you realize that I will be right there in the room the night of the show? And I can tell you, because naturally I've got the inside information, that it is going to be one of the most outstanding TV shows ever produced. You will see, so prepare to be spellbound. The best actors have been hired, the best director and adaptor, and thousands of dollars have been spent. There are dozens of actors and actresses, all of whom have had to spend *weeks* memorizing their lines, so you can just imagine what a first-class production it is going to be. I want you to enjoy every minute of it.

See you Friday. My love to dad and Dee,

[*enclosure to his mother, from* The Foghorn, *October* 19]

PROFESSOR OF ENGLISH PASSES IN SLEEP

Funeral services will be held Monday in Ogden, Utah, for Dr. Elvin R. Outerbridge, who was stricken in sleep last Wednesday. He had been a member of the Department of English since 1929. Death was attributed to a heart attack.

Dr. Outerbridge, who was 64, was born in Ogden, completed his education at Brigham Young University and the University of Chicago, served in World War One, and was a widely-known Biblical figure.

Among his works are *Job: A Disquisition, Benjamin Franklin's Orthodoxy,* and *The Christian Ethic in San Francisco's Chinatown,* and numerous articles.

Professor Holt C. Gamble, Chairman, Department of English, declared that "Dr. Outerbridge is one without whom we hesitate to proceed," while Assistant Professor Lee W. Youngdahl declared that his death "is not to be borne." University President Carlton J. Stamish pointed out that Dr.

Outerbridge was "one of America's steadfast friends to liberal enlightenment."

Dr. Outerbridge's widow, Mrs. Clarice Outerbridge, will return to resume residence in San Francisco. A son, Ralph, is a member of the faculty at the University of Missouri, Columbia, Missouri, and a second son, Wolfe, is a resident of Los Gatos.

Wednesday, October 24

[from Louis Garafolo, Kurman's Camp, Peekskill, N. Y.]

October 21

Dear Lee,

I showed the lawyer what you said, and he said no trouble at all. He will send you a contrack and Dee one. You can see for yourself what the situation of money is when I read in the paper a statement of Cus D'Amato. Quotation. Fighters and managers more and more are getting wiser to the fact that in its campaign of intimidation and rewards, the IBC keeps worthy fighters starving and inferior fighters picking up television matches. The most the average heavyweight can hope to make under the IBC system is $20,000 a year.

I will be glad to see you here, but I expeck you to keep your mouth shut except when eating and me do all the handling of Irwin necessary. I will watch your play on TV and don't see why you think I won't. I want to see anything you write, I don't care if it's about midgets.

I am glad to see you turn over 50% of your share to Dee. I will tell you something I don't think should make you mad any more, but I always thought Dee was a better fighter than you were, and I told your father. I told your father I could have made Dee a title. I told you in Boston hit him with your left hand, but your father kept shouting up at you hit him with your right hand, and Dee kept shouting up at you and trying to cry louder than your father, me and Dee against your father, but then you listened to your father instead of listening to Dee and me, and that was the end of you. Your father said you could not lose because all the Mormons in Utah were down on their knees, and I said now he is down on his knees with the rest of the Mormons. You were. Luckily Alexander Irwin's father is in Alabama. Dee could never beat you because you told him he couldn't, but he could. No matter what you told him he believed. You stole Dee's girls while he was carrying your bags. I see where the girl from Shoshone become a star hit. In those days if your brain would have been as big as your mouth you would have been a wonder, but don't be mad at me and stay in health.

[*from Gabriella Bodeen, New York*]

October 22

Professor darling,

I was afraid your letter would scold me and grade me F, but I did, just for you, stay with the television Puncher as long as I could. The man said, "For God's sake, girl, you play it different every day. Please play it the same way every day, because you mix everybody up from rehearsal to rehearsal," and I said to the man, "For God's sake, boy, that's the only way of playing anything or it." The man said, "You throw off the cameras." "To," burst out I, "hell with the cameras, I have only one short beautiful life to give, and I will not give it away to a camera," and they weeped and cried and teared their hair, but all the same I quit. "Well anyhow," the man said, "you were too big for the part anyhow," and I replied in my violest language, "Pooh," and they hired the loveliest girl with the biggest bosom which will drip over into all the living-rooms in Ogden and Shoshone and thereabouts, and everybody will love them.

New paragraph. You say of your brother, whom or who I think of now you say of, who was studying green things even then; and she or her you mention who or whom I hate, and such a match we would have made, thy and I, and why was it not I instead of how it was, or maybe it was better as it was and is, but anyhow I hate her truly truly.

You won't like Enright when you meet him. He is rich and can hire many people to tell him he is also brilliant. Welcome to the city. And you will feed me meat, and we will walk when all is home in bed in autumn mornings, and up and down to dawn and round and round on all the silent streets, and when the light is up, and people too is up from bed and off to work we will be different from they all, except I hope we will not wrestle in elevators, and you will not reason nor persway me, because if you do I will ring the EMERGENCY BUTTON and make a public seen and scream. O promise me to do not tell me that you love me, and it is only, after all, for friendship and for warmth, because I have many friends and blankets.

My father retired, and he and mother have migrated to Shoshone, two miles from farm to city, and they feel very big-town now. Good Lord, they might yet wind up in sinful Pocatello. My sister's husband won some kind of a prize from the Government and Rockefeller whereby he goes around the world examining mice somebody gave cancer to, and she goes with him and helps him and picks them right up in her hands. My brother is teaching athaletics as he calls them at old Shoshone High and traveling just all *over* Idaho in basketball time.

"Sweet Girl" keeps playing and playing. The stage door is down a tricky alley. Next door to the theater is a cigar store. Go into the cigar store, and out the side, and *then* down the alley. The alley doesn't reach the street. If this should be too confusing for a man who reads and writes as many books as most people in Idaho ever dreamed of buy a cigar and ask the man. He knows everything.

Anticipatorily,

[to Miss Malvina Yodell, San Francisco]

October 24

Dear Miss Yodell,

Bernice and Bernique are a little concerned about your fears that their trip to Utah will interrupt their study of long-division.

I have tried to relieve their concern, and I should like to do the same for your fears, by promising that I shall tutor them as we travel. Their grandmother, whose excellence in long-division is unquestioned, will continue the work in Utah during November.

Bernique and Bernice speak so highly of you that I am encouraged to divulge to you a small family secret: when I was a little boy, and had no luck with long-division, my father, instead of permitting doubts about myself to accrue in my mind, assured me that I was really very *good* in long-division, with the result that I came to believe I was. I learned not to fear it, and to relax with it, until today, while I am by no means an *expert* at it, I am no worse at it than most of the neighbors.

I want to thank you again for your warm and generous interest in my girls, and for your hospitality to me when I visited your class. When I return from the East I should like to visit again, and I hope you will permit me to tell the children more stories, for I have a great surplus.

With best personal regards,

Thursday, October 25

[from Harold Rosenblatt, New Haven, Conn.]

October 23

Dear Lee,

Sylvia and I have your letter of the 20th, which explicates, at least at the dramatic, visual level, your inordinate ingratitude toward Paul, and the reason for my mysterious telephone call to him. We have, also, an inundation of letters, cards, and a telegram—an inundation similar to the one we experienced during our Edinburgh year. At Edinburgh we posted your missiles upon nails on the wall of our cottage, and in idle moments, as one might stroll before pictures in a gallery, we strolled in review before them. I sent you, then, picture-postcards of the Scots countryside, and they inflamed you and elicited from you your rain of fact and fancy, and I in my slow scholar's fashion formed of the scattered parts a whole, and there you were. Now here you are again, and I do not like it.

So you see, I do not "cast" you "aside" at all. Probably I should not write you even now except that the time would seem to have come to approach the parts—the puzzle. I am hoping this letter will reach you before you steam off on your vague mission to New York. Stay where you are.

I have not for a moment believed that you are

seriously worried about your tenure, although I suppose you must often be a bit rattled by all the irresponsible literary discussion of the cramping effects of a university environment. I see you standing at the corner of Eighteenth and Diamond, your manuscript in the mail. Then you drift to school. Where else could you have drifted? Once upon a time artists were supported by churches; Johnson had the King's pension; in this American year, however, the colleges and universities have by a process of historical development come to assume the task formerly assigned to churches and royalty; more important, they provide the artist with his society, his audience: the Coffee Bar is your platform, as Johnson's was the London tavern. There you test your notions, flinging them up against better minds (not better imaginations) than your own. We make you. "If, therefore," Johnson told Boswell, "the profession you have chosen has some unexpected inconveniencies, console yourself by reflecting that no profession is without them . . ."

Idle, you sought conflict. "My leisure has set affairs in motion . . ." It always does. Writers, I think, seek problems to create (so do scholars), must manufacture conflict, for without conflict there can be no drama. But you err to seek it within the minds of your colleagues: your enemies are very few. You are far from our best scholar (you are no scholar at all) and you may not be our most perfect teacher, but you, whose door, whose cabinets are always open, whose correspondence lies scattered about, whose keys are always in their locks (unless they be outside in your ignition), you who in your limitless confidence own no briefcase, carry no notes, nor wear the honor pins nor the titular badges of your profession—tell me who can dare to vote against your openness? What combination of five or three can possibly be found to deny your value?

On that issue I would not be drawn into discussion, nor upon the issue of Harvard, where you would be most unhappy with your shoelaces dragging. Nor will I exchange Journals with you, for yours would glow with invention. Nor will I gallop around Yale in pursuit of two blue beans in a blue bladder while you, at the Coffee Bar, excite everyone with the slapstick spectacle of Harold leading the Yale Boswellians in spirited pursuit of two non-existent blue beans in a non-existent blue bladder. Someone says I have a heart of stone? Am I to check off upon my fingers my possible enemies, wrangle in my mind with each, erect memories of moments in which I might have offended?

Peggy and Oliver are breaking the marriage laws. This I can believe. George Cofax has grown a mustache. This I can believe. Clinch is writing quatrains against his father. This I can believe. (I saw a rather nice poem of his the other day, however, in *The Yale Review*.) Red Traphagen says something about baseball that I cannot understand. This I can believe. *The Foghorn* will be published twice a week. This I can believe. You are going to murder Cecile. This—for the moment —I set aside.

You promise me that I shall be a footnote to your fame. It is an invitation to diagnose you, to study you, to chart your soul; but allow me to point out, if you will, that it was not the scholar Johnson who gave everlasting life to the adventurer Boswell: it was the reverse. And so it is not for me to penetrate you, but for you, Sir, to glorify *me*. It is *you* who are the writer, you who must see the drama which is me. Wake up, Stupid!

Your method is the method of energy. You write, write, write, write, write, and when you are "idle" you write letters and postcards upon your avenue to revelation. It remains for me to illuminate your discovery once you have made it. I did wait.

It would seem to have something to do with Paul. You know (though I assure you we discuss other phenomena, too), Paul and I have sometimes questioned whether you have actually had an affair with Cecile. Now you are about to "murder" her, I to conclude that the affair you have had is over.

But I conclude no such thing because (this might hurt just a little) I don't believe you have ever had an affair with Cecile or with anybody else. Certainly Paul and I have always hoped against it, not because we very much care who screws whom, but because we know how all that you and Beth have had and have done and have and are doing together has always been so binding right. You are still having an affair with your wife. Wisely she has never let you know that you have won her. I have never heard her praise you, tell you all the complimentary things others tell you; your equal she is, but not your fan; she has never subsumed her life to yours, and so she remains for you yet to conquer, and you never shall: probably it was why you chose her in the first place.

But you have thought to tease Paul and me by hint and innuendo, oblique references to clandestine afternoons, your means, I suppose, of telling us you have won Beth, or, more likely, only a hangover from boyhood days in Utah, where manhood was measured in that misguided way. We have always thought you man enough, except insofar as you felt the need to "prove" it.

I suppose, for Paul (we talked low of this on the telephone, at your expense), there was still the last whisper of a single doubt ("Whoyoucallit . . . Cecile"), but then you had the nastiness to shatter his sense of certainty; and after that the additional callousness to make light of his distress. You cannot do this to a man except in a cause of over-riding importance, and only then when the man is a knave. To have done it to Paul, who has labored for weeks upon your play, loves it and understands it as well as you, was a foul act redeemed only by your quick retraction; it threatens your future with him; and it surprises me, for while you have humiliated and embarrassed enemies who are frauds, hoaxes, and liars, I have never known you to work this kind of abuse upon a friend.

What was your real reason for it? It must have been urgent. What was it? Tell me. Better yet, tell yourself.

If you invite me, as you have, to operate upon your brain, you must expect that I shall cut you deep or not at all, and you will therefore pardon the briskness of this letter.

I am sorry about Mr. Outerbridge.

I have received the carbon copy of your play, which is full of high comic talk, and love, and fine motion. I hear flutes and Scottish catches. My admiration for your art swells and increases, which is platitudinous. I shall write you soon again (if you still want me to write you at all) in greater detail, but for the present I can tell you that I find nothing in it to protest upon the grounds of your research: once we accept Boswell and Johnson in Manhattan the rest rings undeviatingly true. I am every inch convinced.

The weather turns chill, and I wince at the thought of winter. The rascals who rented us this house told us the fuel bill, in the coldest month, will not exceed $25, but the gas company tells us we will be lucky if it stays below $30. The kids are picking up Ivy-League accents and manners, unlike Sylvia and me, who, though we manage an expedient protective coloration, gasp for the looser California society.

We won't be going to New York, nor to Peekskill, and I don't know why you're going, either. Do *you* know why?

Fondest regards always,

[*from Abner Klang, New York, special delivery*]

October 24 Lee I wing this to you special to reach you beFore you start out. I wired you the name oF the agency which agencies the Auntie Marie show. What's up.

I sent your bank $1250 covering travel expenses From Enright. First he wanted to give me $500. I said who did he think he was dealing with. Did he think with some First novelist From some junior high school in Kansas City. I pointed out he was dealing with a certain Dr. Lee Youngdahl doctor of philosophy and Famous scholar. Did he think Dr. Youngdahl was coming to New York hitch hiking. Did he think a Famous scholar and philosopher when he came to New York begged in the streets and slept in the sewers. He raised the sum. When Dr. Youngdahl or any other Famous scholar comes to New York they expect a certain respect For their positions From us ordinary slobs that barely picked up a lousy bachelor oF arts. He raised the sum again. IF it was somebody else I wouldn't raise the question but I would be blushing with shame to ask Dr. Youngdahl to skimp and scrimp along on cheap wines and table scraps or expect him to ride down there in the black hole of Calcutter that we call a subway or walk around in rags and tatters. Finally he raised it to $1250. No agency commission. Make sure your bank puts it in.

We are waiting here For you with bells on. You will be at The Brown and everything is like you wish with hot and cold running typewriter in your room and everybody advised as to your desires and sub desires. I also have time tables to and Fro Peekskill. I also have an appointment with you From some jerks From Harvard and also numerous magazines and newspapers wanting to see you not to mention Enright.

I also obtained all the necessary inFormation as to times on Sweet Girl so you can consort with that Fine Female Friend of yours Bodeen who didn't even have the simple honest decency to stick with your show. She cost you a million viewers and you can thank her For me. Don't mention my name.

I Finally got Whizzer Harlow on the ball down in Mexico and he is whipping up stories as Fast as I can sell them. I sold one to Esquire and one to Madamoiselle For $1000 each. Why don't you whip up a Few short stories as long as you're not doing anything. I hope he will stay with it this time and not end up in some kind oF a brawl and go lamming oFF to another part oF the world. A man has got to sit still as I always told him.

A business man is. No time For jokes. Researching around in my Files I located the end oF the joke you mention and send it along herewith. I hope you didn't lose the First part. I still laugh.

Ever yours,

[*enclosure from Abner Klang, New York, concluding fragment to his letter of October 5, received October 7*]

cry and he says why are you crying and she says she is crying because she likewise never be ore engaged in marital delectation and is thinking about her husband and three children back home in Greenwich across the state line where the taxes are cheaper. Both o them are now crying their eyes out. In act all the way to Miami they cry and cry and uck and uck.

Ever yours,

[*special delivery*]

October 25

Mr. W. Wycherly Wood
@ Front Desk
Elyria Hotel
Elyria, Ohio

Dear Wood:

I am empowered by our Department Chairman, Holt C. Gamble, to offer you a position, effective immediately. Will you please wire him or phone him, collect, notifying him of your acceptance or rejection of the position, which I shall here describe in a most general way, and with some apology for my haste, but I am scheduled to depart in an hour on academic business to New York. I hope you will accept and not reject.

Your salary will be in the neighborhood of $4,100. There is also the possibility of summer-school on a part-time basis, although I don't urge you to count upon this, since most of the senior members of the staff need the work—ground to death as they are by avaricious wives whose happiness is apparently proportionate to the number of monstrous immovable objects they own. You will begin at the ignominious snake-belly bottom by teaching three courses in freshman English. Some teachers, since they are dullards, find these courses dull, but you, I suspect, will transform them into surveys in W. Wycherly Wood I, W. Wycherly Wood II, and W. Wycherly Wood III.

When I was in your humble position I made of those courses experimental laboratories in which I sailed aloft ideas for my dissertation, challenging the kids to shoot them down; what they couldn't shoot down I combined into a dissertation. For freshmen, a gentleman as quick as you ought to be able to cook up an hour's bright conversation from what the man before you left on the blackboard.

You seem to be perplexed to find a dissertation topic, and I would like to suggest something I've long mused, and which I shall be pleased to discuss with you after my return here about December 1: have you thought of uniting your interest in American literary biography to your interest in sporting life? What is it that thrusts Mark Twain and Sherwood Anderson into one stream, and Henry James into another? Can you imagine Henry James swabbing horses? It has so much to do—doesn't it?—with a man's early relationship to the society of boys and games—that miniature of our larger society of men and business, with its codes and rules, its provision for imagination within those rules, with winning, losing, timing, bluffing, feinting, jockeying, with directness of aim and speech and with coming back off the floor again. I'm not selling James short, but I *am* saying that some of us seem to belong here, and some go off to

England, and I think it might be traced with fair conviction back to the schoolyards. It's a hasty theory, but I'll do more thinking about it if you take to it, and you'll also get some help from Red Traphagen (the N. Y. Mammoth coach) who, as you may know, teaches the Fall semester in our Department. I do hate to see you get hung up on the dissertation now that you've cleared all the other hurdles. (Little sports jargon right there.)

The job is permanent. Hardly anybody ever gets fired. You come up for Tenure in five years, but if you've been disciplined enough to work through on the PhD your Tenure is all but automatic because if you've stood it five years you've got it made: some people leave sooner: can't stand the truth. We talk pretty free, and they don't like it, and we don't seem to invite them to our parties, and pretty soon they go away. Naked Darwinism.

You'll have to sign a California Loyalty Oath, promising not to overthrow the State. Since you have already tried to overthrow the States of Nebraska and Ohio you have realized the futility of that kind of childish nonsense, and now you are ready to settle down and overthrow California in that private clashroom way where all us bolsheviks do our work. Revolutions every day, and never any blood. Our President fights off the Legislature, has restored a lot of "old-fashioned" things like Latin to the catalogue, and has successfully emasculated the old normal-school contingents of half-wits, dim-wits, nit-wits, tit-mice and tom-tits who used to accept theses entitled "Forty-Nine

Janitorial Services in the Public Schools of Redwood City."

Then, of course, San Francisco is San Francisco. Everybody isn't deliriously happy here every minute of every day, but unhappiness is moderated by the weather and simplified by the great infusion here of all racial and national groupings and refugees from New York, who give us big-time shops and theaters and bookstores without any of the disadvantages of big-time congestion. My experienced observation is that our women equal any ladies of the world for stylishness, lusciousness and good humor (a hundred streets here are named for girls). There is no through traffic to speak of, no factories to speak of (because no through railroads), and so we are, among other things, the cleanest city on the face of America: our garbage we ship across the Bay to Oakland for export to Los Angeles.

Speaking of trains reminds me I must go. Pardon my ramble. Anyhow, please inform our Chairman. For myself, I am hoping you will come You will like it here.

Yours very truly,

[*to his wife, San Francisco*]

ABOARD "THE CITY OF SAN FRANCISCO," en route *to Ogden*

October 25

Dear Beth,

As I was kissing you goodby in Oakland I happened to notice, over your shoulder, a beautiful lady kissing her husband goodby. Her name is Mrs. Galloway (I call her Nance, which is the affectionate form of Nancy), she lives in the Avenues, she has three children, and she was surprised to learn I am as young as I am, since she had formed the notion, from *The Hard Puncher,* that the author was not the boxer but the boxer's father. I assured her that I am not my father, and I accused her of not buying the book, for, had she *bought* it, she would have seen my photo on the jacket. She confessed to membership in the public library.

Lucien calls me a blockhead, an epithet he has picked up from the *Life,* from which he has not lifted his eyes since dinner, and I fear we may soon have another Johnsonian on our hands. Bernique and Bernice are at their division, and all else are fine and window-watching.

To be continued.

In the club car after all but Nance and I had gone to bed (her compartment, I might mention, adjoins) we were addressed by a traveling man in the following manner:

"Folks, where are you bound?"

"Ogden, Utah," I replied.

"Young man, what's your work?"

"I'm a Secret Service Man," I said.

"You don't say?"

"I do say."

"You're not behaving in a very secret way."

"I'm on vacation."

"When you're not on vacation what do you do?"

"I guard the President," I said.

"From what?" he said.

"From assassination."

"Who'd want to assassinate the President?"

"Assassins."

"Why?"

"To fulfill themselves," I said.

"What does your wife think of that sort of work?"

"It's a living," Nance said.

"Well, now," said the traveling man, "tell me, if you possibly can, without lying, just exactly what you'd do if an assassin jumped out with a gun in his hand. Don't evade, don't evade. You saw it was you or him, and you thought of your lovely wife and your beautiful children . . ."

"It's a question we often ask ourselves," I said.

"You and your wife?"

"My wife and I, and all the wives and all the husbands in the Secret Service."

"The assassin is standing there, the gun is in his hand, he's pointing. PAM!"

"I'd jump in front of him," I said.

"Don't lie, don't lie."

"I'd jump in front—"

"You're lying!"

"*Sideways,*" I said.

Now the porter comes to tell me I must go, for he must lock his car. He tells me I may begin drinking again at six in the morning if I so desires. However, he cautions me of my mistake in thinking of him as a porter: he is a Club Car Attendant.

On my desk at school is a letter received there this morning from Harold. You may read it if you wish. You may also kiss Tetsey for me if you wish. Or, time permitting, you may do both. Now I really *must* go because the Club Car Attendant is giving me a very mean look.

Your friend,

P.S. Don't stew over Harold's letter. Hope he doesn't come down to New York and annoy me. As if I'd just pick up and race off to New York without sternly calculating every step. Connecticut air decaying his mind. I'll avoid him if he does. Comes down I mean. Doubt if he will.

Friday, October 26

[*to a group of his children*]

ABOARD THE UNITED AIRLINES MAINLINER 646,
Salt Lake to New York

October 26

Dear Lucien, Bernique, Bernice, Thornton, Glenna, and Earl,

Goodness, what excitement! By now, however, you are all asleep and dreaming, while I have the honor of flying right smack over the center of the whole United States, which I think is just about the only country left that still dreams dreams.

If I were home at this moment I might go for a walk. However, if I were to try to go for a walk right now it would be 9,000 feet to the sidewalk, so I think I've changed my mind.

When I came into this airplane it was quiet. The propellors were not turning. The motor was not roaring. Then the propellor began to turn rather slowly, and the motor began to hum, but low. It did not seem to me to be strong enough to fly, and I had half a mind to rush out the door and take the train.

However, by a stroke of luck, just at that instant the motor stopped humming—and began roaring, and the propellors began to whirr a little faster. Still, I said, as it began to move along the ground, "Posh, you blockhead, anybody can move along the *ground*. The question is, Can you get up into the *air?*"

No reply.

"Sure, sure, that's a nice big noise you're making, and I see you flapping your wings, but can you *fly?* If you can't fly you have no business calling yourself an airplane, you old groundplane, you."

At this she became very angry. Now she roared. Now she spun those propellors like mad. Now she shivered and shook and vibrated and quivered until I thought she would explode from all her effort. For just a moment she stood perfectly still, looking about her at the bright lights, and up into the air at the stars in the dark night, and then she took a deep, deep, d-e-e-e-p breath, and she poured flames from her wings, and they were bright and red and angry—very angry—and then she raced with unimaginable speed along the ground, and I calmly said, "But can you lift? Can you *lift?*"

Again, no reply. But she lifted, and without even looking back at me—positively ignoring me—she haughtily tucked her legs up under her, and off she sailed, and she hasn't come down yet. Ah me, I am defeated again.

A nice young lady brings me coffee. A little while ago she saw *The Hard Puncher* on television. I said I also saw it. She says it was one of the best television shows she ever saw in her life. I said my children liked it real well, and she told me that the author of it was born in Ogden, and I said I had heard a rumor to that effect.

I told her I think this is a most marvelous airplane, but she doesn't think so at all. To her, there is nothing marvelous about drinking coffee and writing a letter 9,000 feet in the air. I don't know why, but this girl feels very sad and defeated about things, and I have been cheering her up.

Everything is marvelous. Notice how this is true in and around Ogden. When Grandpa's grandfather came to Utah he said, "This is the place." Of course, what he really meant was, "This can *be* the place," and he *made* it the place, people like him and Grandpa's father and Grandpa and Uncle Dee. It was because they dreamed. If you meet anybody that tells you things are not marvelous, or we should all feel sad and defeated, or life is no good and we might as well blow everybody up—well, tell them I say they're blockheaded.

Please do what Uncle Dee says about horses. I know that you all know a great deal about horses, but Uncle Dee knows a great deal *more*. He is the only man I know who not only understands horse language but the finest grammatical *points* of horse language. So if you listen to him you will be safe.

Will Lucien please give Thornton spelling words. Bernique and Bernice, please look at the long-division once in awhile.

I forgot to leave spending money for you, so please ask Grandma to give each of you one dollar, and I will pay her back. Make the dollar last until Mother comes.

Please all line up, and everybody give everybody a kiss from me.

With great love to my marvelous children,

Saturday, October 27

[to his wife, San Francisco]

THE BROWN
A SMALL HOTEL

October 27

Dear Beth,

This is the place, although I dislike some of the people. Enright wears a porkpie hat with a little red feather in it, and shirts of pale pink, and fifty-dollar red bowties. Abner urges me to take more kindly to Enright, for he is rich—Abner whose desires are as clear and as straight and as true as always, and who does not dress himself in colors. "Let's talk business," Abner says, and so we did all afternoon, but I have still not signed.

Enright had a play doctor with him. "Who's sick?" I said. "Why are we playing doctor?"

"This is Steve Zippke," Enright said.

"It's hard to believe," I said.

Zippke complains that not enough things are explained in my play. He also complains that it ought to be in two acts, or, better yet, three, because it's what everybody expects, especially the orange-juice concessionaires. He further complains that it lacks a love interest, and when I suggest that the love interest involves Johnson and Boswell he informs me that there is already an over-supply of fairy plays on Broadway.

Principally Enright and I debated whether, according to the laws of tradition and the code of the Dramatists Guild, I may or may not allow Paul to continue with the University Theater production while negotiating a Broadway contract. I say I may, and Enright says I mayn't, and Abner sulks. We arrived nowhere.

Slipped away and saw *Sweet Girl,* which is in two well-paced acts, which cues the audience on nothing, and which concerns a country girl who learns to charm men by appealing, one after another, to their diverse political prejudices. The people come and cover up the seats, and the show keeps running by virtue of a small, discriminating following. The house is small, the sets modest, cast and crew work at the minimum, and everybody seems to be having a good time. Bodeen is very deft and very beautiful, and just the girl for me. She introduced me to the producer—T. T. Tattershall, nice chap—and then we walked about a good bit, she and I, not Tattershall, and talked of how we have risen in the world on the strength of (putting it quietly) our own enormous magnificence and relentless cunning, not to mention absolute sincerity.

Everyone was well when I left Ogden. The house overflowed with Youngdahls who had come from as far away as Bingham Canyon to watch me watch my show. I think there were a hundred cousins I have never seen before, nor even heard of, and when the hour came they hushed. Dad set up a camera in front of the set, and when my credits showed (they, at least, were according to my demand)—FLASH FLASH—he shot my credits in the air. The remainder was all Wenk's. Yet, somehow, I could not care, and mother and the kids sat transfixed, and there was silence except when there was laughter, and there were tears, and there was suspense, and there was piety, and there was sentiment, everything, everything, so long as it explored no new emotion. Everybody loved the Puncher, and everybody hated the Irishman, and everybody loved the good girl and hated the bad girl, although I myself was unable to tell the difference, and when it was done they all agreed it was even better than the "real" fights, and I am clearly the Mormon reply to William Shakespeare. "Every man," said Johnson, "has a lurking wish to appear considerable in his native place."

Dee met me at the station with Youngdahls and local reporters, and it was the old Dee, restored to my camp—"Stand back, folks, and let the Desert Rat through"—sold by my letter, brother again. I walked the fences with him, and he is silent, and he studies; he creates those acres; he deliberates upon blades of grass: they are his commas and his semi-colons, sentences, paragraphs, chapters, theme and meaning, and he sees them in their parts, and he sees them whole, and he speaks never a word. Then, suddenly, some problem solved—some square of earth returned to its place in the scheme—he will speak, and he will be free enough of tongue until the problem solved suggests another and a larger, and he will go silent again to his fences. And he must do this every day and every hour.

Enright wants to get together tomorrow, but I have told him it's against my principles to discuss business on the Lord's day. He said he had forgotten it was the Lord's day. I want to go to Peekskill tomorrow and examine my investment. Abner says he hopes it is not against my principles to *think* on the Lord's day, and I told him I will think very hard about changing Boswell to a girl. He requests that I also think about Enright's suggestion that I cut the size of the cast: the average successful play, says Enright, has fewer people in it, and I have told him I will bend every effort to reduce the play to the successful average. We are supposed to meet again Monday, but I'm not sure why. Abner says Whizzer is coming.

It is today here but it is still yesterday there, or else it is today there but tomorrow here. Whichever it is, it is time for bed.

Your confused acquaintance,

Sunday, October 28

[*to Harold Rosenblatt, New Haven, Conn., postcard*]

Sunday the 28

Sure I know why. The reason I came to New York (The Brown: a small hotel) is so that I don't have to sit home and look at your absurd house sitting, or, more exactly, slanting, and about to fall over on its side, and the reason I don't want to look at your house is that it reminds me of you. If you come down to New York I might feel different, but if you don't you nauseate me.

[*to his brother, Ogden, Utah*]

THE BROWN
A SMALL HOTEL

October 28

Dear Dee,

I want to give you a little report on our mutual property. I was up there today, and he looks very good to me. The camp is as it was in the old days, except it now accommodates about ten fighters, mostly Latin Americans, so it's a somewhat larger operation than formerly.

Today everybody was taking things very easy, the excuse being that it is Sunday—everybody, I mean, except Irwin, who was punching the bag and looking around for somebody to fight. He can't stand being idle. He has murdered all his partners, so that Garafolo is having a hard time keeping him stocked. We had some photos taken, and I'll send them along to you as soon as I get them.

This afternoon he went two rounds with a heavy named Capidaglas, formerly the champion of France or some such thing, and Irwin marked him up fairly well until Garafolo put a stop to it.

Still, in my opinion, Irwin can be hurt with the cross over the jab, and I told Garafolo so, but Garafolo doesn't think so. One thing I *do* know, I could be champion of France if I wanted to—and you could be super-champion of France. Well, as Samuel Johnson said, what can you expect of a nation that eats frogs? I punched the bag a bit myself today, worked up a glorious sweat, and feel fine.

Chanced into Gabriella Bodeen, and walked about sixteen miles with her this evening. She's in good shape, too. About every two blocks she asks for you, wishes to be remembered, etc. Irwin reminds me of you, thinking every minute of his work, turning it over and over in his mind. I think he must fight in his sleep. He never misses a day at the bag, and I noticed tonight at the table how he listens: talk about the world, that's not for him; talk about girls, well—maybe he'll sort of lift an eyebrow; but talk about fighting—why, then he stops eating. He is farming, so to speak, every minute, and I admire him immensely.

It's 2 A.M. here but it's only midnight in Ogden. The moral is, Stay in Utah and stay young. Please kiss all the kids for me. I have told them to listen to you on the subject of horses, but if they don't don't hesitate to let fly a couple of soft jabs when necessary. They are very crafty operators.

So much for business,

Monday, October 29

[from his wife, San Francisco]

October 27

Dear Lee,

No comment. What they don't seem to understand is that you don't have to be highbrow. You just have to be convincing, and all the rest will take care of itself. Who ever saw such a rosy-cheeked boxer? Lucien could have punched him silly. Who ever heard such a rosy-cheeked boxer spouting moral teachings between the rounds? I don't think Bodeen or all the Barrymores could have animated that script.

Paul and Willa commiserated with me throughout. The only cheerful news is the enclosed letter from Searle, which I have taken the liberty of showing them. I hope you don't mind, but it was too good not to share, and Tetsey isn't much to share it with.

You should be there by now, and you should have seen *Sweet Girl* by now, and its infamous star, and Alexander Irwin. I'd like to see Irwin and Bodeen go a few rounds together.

Your gentle wife,

[*enclosure from his wife: from Harry Searle*]

October 26

Dear Lee,

I guess I have quite an apology to make because I told you that I would come in and speak to your students for nothing, but now the picture has changed quite a bit. I am now requesting if you can take that $25 fee you offered, but I refused, and make it $50 as I am in quite a jam. Either of the dates you mentioned are quite satisfactory, or any other that meets your needs.

Actually I over-extended my financial situation quite a bit, with the result that I am now forced back into the free-lance field in quite a big way. To save time I began having my girl type over old "Auntie Maria" scripts from eight and nine years ago instead of writing new ones, with the result that I got in quite a jam with the show. The public began writing in complaining, and when they do that you are in hot water, with the result that I am now forced to write completely new stuff. Now my time is quite limited. I think a fee of $50 will pay me for my time, as I must go all the way in from Larkspur, quite a trip, bridge tolls and all considered, simply because the bastards got on me.

A nice big hydrogen bomb right down in the middle of them all would be quite an improvement.

I guess that's the writing game for you, but it's quite a tough blow all the same. Please drop me a card and tell me if the $50 comes within your means. Don't telephone, as I've taken the telephone out as an economy measure. Do you know anybody that wants to buy a wife quite cheap? (Just kidding.)

With warmest personal felicitations,

[*to his wife, San Francisco*]

THE BROWN
A SMALL HOTEL

October 29

Dear Beth,

I started to write you an hour ago, but my beginning was delayed by the entry of Mr. Brown, or Mr. Small, who brought me refreshing liquids and who hopes I will recommend his hotel to literary people, of whom he is very fond. To this moment, he is the only person, except you, who has had the courage to tell me that the television version of *The Hard Puncher* stunk, and in this he is as unfashionable as his hotel. In New York the exercise is to discover what is being said, so that one might say the same. Come to think of it, this was also the London custom except when Johnson introduced into politest circles a salutary perversity. Come to think of it, it is all too often also the University fashion.

I told Dr. Zippke this morning that I will alter Boswell—Jane Boswell he will become—and I will introduce into the play a handyman who at intervals will say, "You mean . . . ?" Then everyone will know just exactly what is meant, as we do on the "Auntie Maria" show. So—Johnson comes to Manhattan with his girl friend, Jane. They are hopelessly in love. . . . I am nothing if not co-operative.

Hilarious thing happened. *Bonanza Boat* having moved to a larger theater, a rehearsal was held this afternoon to accustom all hands to the new site, and I sat through the first act with Enright. (I do so love a dark theater of an afternoon I wish I were a bum.) Although Enright seems to be of the opinion that *Bonanza Boat* is a work of art at least equal to the Sistine Chapel, I could not refrain from telling him I thought the first act at least twice as long as it ought to have been. "Everything," I said, "is too *explained*. Don't you see? After you've established a thing there's no longer any need to *establish* a thing. And after you've established a thing three or six times there's surely no need to establish it nine or twelve." It was therefore with some embarrassment that I discovered, this evening, that what I saw this afternoon was only a walk-through—the merest fragment of a first act which in its public form is three times as long as what was already twice too long.

The music I have heard before. At every point at which a valid emotion is in danger of appearing, the music breaks anew, suffocating a nice idea somebody once had about some people in a seaport town who go spending their money before their ship comes in. They should have kept the idea and thrown out the music. Abner cautions me, however, not to squander my sympathies upon the man whose idea has been sacrificed, for he has become very rich.

It is much easier to do business with Garafolo. I told him in Peekskill yesterday that in my opinion Irwin can be hit with a right hand over the jab. "No he can't," said Garafolo.

"Yes he can," said I.

"No he can't."

"Yes he can."

"No he can't."

"Yes he can."

"Nope."

"Yup."

"No."

"Yes."

With my friend Garafolo there are no small, brown ambiguities.

Walking tonight with Bodeen, I came upon an oat-cake shop. I have sent a box of oat-cakes to Harold, a box to you, and I have myself investigated, to the extent of one oat-cake, a third box. I do not recommend them. By contrast, shredded wheat is an incomparable delicacy. I am of Johnson's opinion about oat-cakes.

I am pleased with the Searle matter. It is laughter on a solemn day.

I have been seen or talked to by various people representing the literary consciousness of local journals, but I find myself becoming faintly irritable. After I have said I was born in Ogden, Utah, it is scarcely exciting to say so again, with the result that I find myself ranging down to Texas, and up to Montana. My age, too, becomes flexible. I have shifted you about with me, toyed with your past in harmless ways, added and subtracted children at will, promoted myself to Chairman of the Department, and founded the San Francisco Quarter-A-Word Club.

Whizzer has just phoned to say that he has stopped for a drink somewhere in Pennsylvania. Perhaps, when he arrives, he will provide fun and purpose.

Your Oklahoma husband,

Tuesday, October 30

[from his wife, San Francisco]

October 28

Dear Secret Service Man,

Today's news, which I enclose, is not so funny as yesterday's.

W. Wycherly Wood, for some reason, instead of phoning Mr. Gamble phoned here to accept, and I have phoned Mr. Gamble. Wood says you "saved my life," and I told him you did no such thing. He's flying, ought to be here in a day or two, in time, I hope, to relieve me of the freshman class, as I'm having all I can do to keep up with the Testament and 18th Century, and Tetsey won't leave me alone for a minute. The empty house frightens her.

I think your Tenure Committee has met, or is going to meet, Paul said which but it didn't register. The Purdys went with Tetsey and me to the zoo. We saw giraffes. Talk about blockheads!

Love,

[*enclosure from Beth*]

INSTRUCTOR, STUDENT KILLED IN AIR CRASH

MONTEREY—The 37-year-old director of an air college and his 21-year-old student were killed yesterday when their two seater dual control airplane crashed in a beet field near here.

Dead were Tremont C. "Tom" Katt, director of Katt's Air College at Monterey, and pretty Nancy G. Baxter, whose parents, Mr. and Mrs. John C. Baxter, make their home in Capitola.

Katt, father of two children, distinguished himself during World War Two and the Korean Conflict, and held a reserve commission in the Air Forces. In April he was reprimanded by San Francisco police and CAA officials for flying a glider between the towers of the Golden Gate Bridge.

Miss Baxter was a senior at San Jose State College and hoped to become the first woman commercial airlines pilot. Katt was training her for that position. Her father teaches social studies in the public schools at Capitola.

[*to Harold Rosenblatt, New Haven, Conn.*]

THE BROWN
A SMALL HOTEL

October 30

Dear Harold,

I have sent you a box of genuine Scottish oat-cakes. They are inedible. However, a man of your insensitivity will never notice.

Tom Katt is dead (see enclosed).

A man from the New York *Herald Tribune* asks me what writer has most influenced my life. I told him Harold Rosenblatt. He said, "Who in hell is Harold Rosenblatt?" I said he is Sylvia Rosenblatt's husband. Then he asked for a great many biographical details about you, which, being unable to supply, I invented. I told him you are presently smuggling the Boswell papers out of Yale to California. Yale will get a big laugh out of it all, and you may be back in California sooner than you think.

Happy Hallowe'en,

[*enclosure to Harold Rosenblatt: newspaper item, dateline Monterey*]

[*to Paul Purdy, San Francisco*]

THE BROWN
A SMALL HOTEL

October 30

Dear Paul,

Enright and I are walking down Broadway. Actors and actresses, playwrights, directors, and real-estate operators are clutching at him for a word. "Go way," he says, "or I'll break your neck." We enter a theater to see his show, *The Family Place,* which, his friends tell him, is the greatest psychological drama since *Macbeth.* The usher erroneously leads us to the wrong seats. Enright threatens to break the usher's neck.

The curtain rises on a very elaborate set, wherein we discover a mother and a daughter and a son. The mother explains to the son that she is his mother. The mother explains to the daughter that she (the mother) is her (the daughter's) mother. The son and the daughter explain to each other that they are brother and sister. They then explain to each other that father has for some years been in a madhouse. A psychiatrist arrives and explains that he is an old friend of the family and a psychiatrist. The psychiatrist says, "We all have fears, even psychiatrists."

I say, "Mr. Enright, my name is Dr. Lee Youngdahl and I am leaving."

He says, "Where are you going?"

I say, "I am going down the street and see *Sweet Girl.*"

He says, "I am grossing six times as much."

The psychiatrist says, "We all have fears."

I say, "He already said that twice."

The mother says she is the mother and fears that her daughter does not love her, but that her son loves her too much. The daughter says she fears her mother hates her father, but that she—the daughter—loves her father too much. The psychiatrist explains that this is incest and more or less normal. The son says that he fears that he is in love with a fellow on the lacrosse team at Amherst. The psychiatrist says this is homosexuality and more or less normal, and my mind begins to float toward Ogden, Utah, where, obviously, we are none of us normal, too busy to be normal—raising families, farming, somehow relating to the civic processes without worrying whether we are loving everyone too much or too little. Maybe we ain't very literary, but we are surviving, and I am wondering if these Broadway issues are the issues of our life, or these people the people of the country. Where anyhow, Paul, do these playwrights *find* all these homosexual marijuana addicts and Lesbian Buddhists?

Drinking orange pop in the lobby I say, "Mr. Enright, something is making me sick."

"It is the orange juice," he says, "I'll break their neck."

"Maybe," I say, "it is your pale pink shirt."

"How are you enjoying the show?" he asks, but he is not looking at me. He is enfolding in his arms scores of dear friends whose names he does not know who are telling him what a marvelous show it is. While he is not looking at me I disappear into the street.

I have a fascination with health. The themes of the present theater do not seem to be my themes, nor to be the themes of the circle I know. I like *Sweet Girl,* in which a healthy young lady gets the man she's after by coolly resigning herself to the realistic fact that certain kinds of people just don't and can't and never will spiritually or chemically combine with certain others. She and I and Tattershall have been ushering in the dawns together, and I think he will come out to San Francisco and see *Boswell's Manhattan Journal* when you've once got it in seeable shape. Could you put him up? Or could you make a reservation for him in Ducey Hall?

Exactly why I'm here I do not know. I may even cut it short and go back and ride horses in Utah. Don't tell Mr. Gamble, however. I thank you for keeping Beth company, but, on the other hand, I want you to leave her leisure enough to discover how badly she misses me. A scholar wrote of Boswell that when he went seriously to work on the *Life* he "achieved a discipline of purpose, and was organized and integrated in a definite direction." When Boswell was idle he was disorganized and disintegrated in an indefinite direction. Work. Work. WORK. Work work work work work work, keep busy—you know, I think that's what my play is about—work, work, involve yourself in the life outside yourself, and the life inside yourself will unite with the life outside yourself, and *there* will be your art. (A magazine writer asked me the other day what I considered significant about myself, and I said, "I always write facing a window." Now I understand what I meant. I am facing a window even now, as I write to you.) And so to bed.

My love to you and Willa,

Wednesday, October 31

[*from Abner Klang, by messenger*]

Tuesday nite. Lee you had better square away beFore everything is ruined. Where are you. In case you are interested your wiFe called and I was hounded to death all day by these pests From Harvard. A man like you can drive a man to suicide any minute. You are ambivalent. I told your wiFe I did not know where you were and Harvard the same. Nobody believed me. What an irony. In the course oF conversation money was mentioned and I was Flabbergasted to hear that iF you went there you would receive $10000 at the outside whereas I can get you that For thirteen weeks on a picture. You are Failing to make the most oF your opportunities as I told your wiFe. You have got to be more aFFirmative with Enright. Don't walk out on his shows any more. Go back with him and sit through them. Tell him you had a headache. Show appreciation. Laugh out loud at all jokes and so Forth until we sign and don't call him a Communist any more. Leave politics out of it. You also called Wenk the same. Nobody can locate you. What were you telling Tattershall. I couldn't believe my ears. IF you are paying halF oF his expenses to San Francisco I will be the laughing stock oF every agent and I cannot believe you would go out oF your way to hurt my bargaining position by an insanity oF that variety. It is unbelievable. I just phoned. I am coming over in the morning and hope to Find you there. Where are you.

Ever yours,

[*to his wife, San Francisco*]

THE BROWN
A SMALL HOTEL

October 31

Dear Beth,

Scene: a small hotel. Lee Youngdahl is eating breakfast in bed. He is alone. He is reading *The Life of Sheffield.* Enter Mr. Brown or Mr. Small.

MR. BROWN OR MR. SMALL: Lee, I don't mean to interrupt, but a Mr. Harlow is here to see you and won't be denied.

YOUNGDAHL: Send him up.

MR. BROWN OR MR. SMALL: He's already up.

YOUNGDAHL: Then send him in.

WHIZZER: I'm in.

MR. BROWN OR MR. SMALL: May I come in, too?

YOUNGDAHL: Sure, come on in, too.

MR. BROWN OR MR. SMALL: Because I do so relish literary conversation.

YOUNGDAHL: By the way, Tom Katt's dead.

WHIZZER: Again?

YOUNGDAHL: This time for keeps.

WHIZZER: Sure.

YOUNGDAHL: Have some coffee. Why didn't

you stay in Santa Fé? Now you've gone and loused everything up.

WHIZZER: How?

YOUNGDAHL: Just by coming.

WHIZZER: I'll go. I don't have to put up with you.

YOUNGDAHL: Have some coffee first, then go.

MR. BROWN OR MR. SMALL: It's so interesting to hear literary men talk.

YOUNGDAHL: He's no literary man. A literary man stays at his desk.

WHIZZER: I had a big fight with Hector La Paz. He irks the hell out of me.

YOUNGDAHL: A literary man doesn't have big fights with his benefactor. You didn't see Samuel Johnson letting the King irk the hell out of him. Where's my $450?

WHIZZER: You met any nice girls in town?

YOUNGDAHL: Hundreds. Last night I had thirty girls right in this room.

MR. BROWN OR MR. SMALL: No he didn't, he's only joking.

YOUNGDAHL: Well, I had fifteen, or seven and a half.

WHIZZER: You mind if I shave? Where's your razor?

YOUNGDAHL: Two into seven goes three, two into a half goes—you can't do it, you can't halve seven and a half.

WHIZZER (from bathroom): Where's your cream?

MR. BROWN OR MR. SMALL: Three and three-quarters.

YOUNGDAHL: I had three and three-quarters girls in here.

WHIZZER: Sounds interesting.

MR. BROWN OR MR. SMALL: He did not.

YOUNGDAHL: You just said so yourself.

WHIZZER: I heard him.

YOUNGDAHL: How much you want to bet Katt's dead? I'll tell you what I'll do. You got any money with you?

WHIZZER: I got lots. I sold three stories.

YOUNGDAHL: I'll bet you the $450 you owe me. If he's dead you pay me, if he's not we're square.

WHIZZER (rushing excitedly from bathroom, in a lather): How'll we prove it?

YOUNGDAHL: Is it a bet?

WHIZZER: Sure.

YOUNGDAHL (to Mr. Brown or Mr. Small): You're a witness. OK, call California. I'll pay for the call.

WHIZZER: What time is it in California?

YOUNGDAHL: It's ten twenty-eight.

WHIZZER: Where?

YOUNGDAHL: Here.

MR. BROWN OR MR. SMALL: Then it's seven twenty-eight in California.

WHIZZER: What a mind that man has!

Enter Abner Klang, a literary agent; Gabriella Bodeen, an actress; T. T. Tattershall, producer of *Sweet Girl* and one devoted to reconciliation between hope and reality: "It needn't necessarily be widely understood," he once was heard to say, "if only we strive with all our might to keep it small."

GABRIELLA (shrieking): Whizzer darling!

ABNER (shrieking): Whizzer!

WHIZZER (at telephone): Bodeen! Abner!

YOUNGDAHL: Cut out the dirty talk.

ABNER: You! Did you get my letter?

YOUNGDAHL: Sure I got your letter.

ABNER: Did you read it?

YOUNGDAHL: Sure I read it.

ABNER: Enough formalities. Give me the manuscript back. Who invited Tattershall? Where is it?

YOUNGDAHL: I haven't got it. It's flying back to California.

ABNER: Why? Why? Somebody tell me why.

YOUNGDAHL: Because it's faster than the train. Have some coffee.

ABNER: Never mind coffee, I already had.

BODEEN: Tattershall darling, sit down. Mr. Brown or Mr. Small, may we have some chairs?

MR. BROWN OR MR. SMALL: Of course. How many?

YOUNGDAHL: Does anybody mind if I get out of bed?

BODEEN: Oh I don't know, just count asses and divide by one.

T. T. TATTERSHALL (examining *The Life of Sheffield*): Who's he?

YOUNGDAHL: An Englishman. You mean you never heard of Sheffield?

T. T. TATTERSHALL: Never.

YOUNGDAHL: Aren't you afraid people will think you're ignorant?

T. T. TATTERSHALL: No.

YOUNGDAHL: Abner, here's a first-rate man. Do business with him.

ABNER (clapping hands): We'll give you six months on option at $2,000.

T. T. TATTERSHALL: I'd like to read the play first. I can't pay that kind of option.

ABNER: Why do you have to read it for? Youngdahl wrote it.

WHIZZER (at telephone): Oh, operator, for Christ's sake.

ABNER: My insane ambivalent client mailed it back to California.

WHIZZER: Bodeen, you get loveli— Damn you, operator. Monterey, the newspaper. No I don't. What's the name of the newspaper in Monterey?

YOUNGDAHL: It's not the Salt Lake *Tribune*. Go home and fix your typewriter why don't you? (He disappears into the bathroom, cleans up the mess Whizzer has left, changes the blade, shaves, and emerges to discover that coffee, Enright, and Zippke have arrived.) Good morning, gentlemen. Meet Mr. Brown or Mr. Small, proprietor of this hotel. Mr. Brown or Mr. Small, this is Mr. Enright and Mr. Zippke, famous Communists.

ENRIGHT: That's a goddam lie.

ZIPPKE: It's a goddam slander.

MR. BROWN OR MR. SMALL: Welcome, welcome, it's a great pleasure I'm sure.

T. T. TATTERSHALL: Ridiculous.

ENRIGHT: *Ridiculous* is no word for it. (Reading newspaper clippings.) Producer contributes to freedom fund. Producer scores Reds.

YOUNGDAHL: Look at that necktie. Look at that shirt. It's the Communist uniform. Red, red, red.

ENRIGHT: Enright on Voice of America. Committee lauds Enright role.

YOUNGDAHL: You printed them yourself.

ENRIGHT: I printed *The New York Times*?

YOUNGDAHL: You're un-American.

ENRIGHT: I'm more American than the Mississippi River.

YOUNGDAHL: The Mississippi River runs in Canada.

ENRIGHT: Like hell it does I think.

YOUNGDAHL: Well, it runs into the Gulf of Mexico, and that's the uniform of the Mexican Communist Party you're wearing.

WHIZZER: Monterey . . . Monterey. Give me the city desk.

ZIPPKE: Monterey? Monterey, *California?* That's my home town. What are you calling Monterey for?

YOUNGDAHL: To talk to it.

ZIPPKE: What for?

WHIZZER: City desk? Say . . . listen . . .

YOUNGDAHL: Did you know Tom Katt?

ZIPPKE: Friend of yours?

YOUNGDAHL: He used to be.

ZIPPKE: What'd you do? Did you call him a Communist? You fight with everybody. You know that?

YOUNGDAHL: He's not a Communist. He was an ill-educated Romantic, and he's dead.

ZIPPKE: Katt? I don't believe it.

YOUNGDAHL: You're another. You Mexican Communists don't believe anything.

ZIPPKE (rising): Listen, buddy.

YOUNGDAHL (rising, removing robe): What?

MR. BROWN OR MR. SMALL: Please, gentlemen, please.

YOUNGDAHL: An American is a man that does what hasn't been tried before. Play it safe, play it safe, play it safe, that's your philosophy, contempt for the human mind, that's your philosophy, and it's Mexican Communism pure and simple.

T. T. TATTERSHALL: I wouldn't say you're reasoning terribly logically.

YOUNGDAHL: I wouldn't say I'm reasoning at all.

WHIZZER (taking three inches of money out of his pocket, counting out $450, and handing it to Youngdahl): Goddam you, anyhow.

YOUNGDAHL (handing money to Abner Klang): Count it.

ABNER: Love to.

YOUNGDAHL (insane with power): The difference between America and Russia is the difference between dramatic principles and mere words. The Russians *say*. Your stinking plays *say*. But a real play *plays,* unfolds. It *acts*. Actions speak louder than words.

WHIZZER: What a clever phrase! Did you just make it up?

GABRIELLA: You better shut up and stay out of it, darling.

WHIZZER: Either he's flipped, he's flipping, or he's about to.

GABRIELLA: Quiet. There's a method in it.

ABNER (returning money): It's all there.

YOUNGDAHL: You're broke and I'm flipping! Don't make me laugh. If you're so smart why ain't you rich? His hat has a red feather in it. Is contempt Communism? Americans are people who don't write to formula like the Wright brothers and Henry Ford. Does the Mississippi River flow in Canada?

MR. BROWN OR MR. SMALL: I'm sure I don't know.

YOUNGDAHL: Then don't participate in the discussion.

ENRIGHT: I'm going.

MR. BROWN OR MR. SMALL: Gentlemen, don't go.

ZIPPKE: Let's go.

T. T. TATTERSHALL: Calm. Some manners.

YOUNGDAHL: I have manners even if they're bad. Bodeen, my pants. Manners! Form, custom, be polite, play it safe, play it safe, don't dare offend anyone, be politic, be cautious, be careful what you say, don't say it if it hasn't been said before, don't try it if it hasn't been tried before, see what's been done and then go do the same, avoid originality, avoid risk, count the costs, truckle to the idiot average. *Adios,* Mexican Communists.

T. T. TATTERSHALL: If you have manners zip up your pants.

Curtain,

Thursday, November 1

[*from his wife, San Francisco*]

October 30

Dear Lee,

A gentleman from Elyria, Ohio, is staying with me. He arrived with his hair standing on end, a change of underwear in his pocket, and his toothbrush marking his place in a copy of *The Hard Puncher*. You saved, he says, his life, the details of which he has lavished upon me in their uncensored entirety. I introduced him to your freshman class, and when I departed from the room he was already totally engaged, his underwear hanging from his pocket. Now he is asleep in Bernique's bed. Tomorrow he goes in search of an apartment. Thursday he starts work on his dissertation. Friday he completes it, and by Saturday he should be President of the University.

In general, he is indistinguishable from some of your better students, and I am wondering about all this talk of a beat generation.

My dear friend, I have examined Harold's letter, but I find no news therein. Goodness, I have seen your eyes roving Cecile's flanks, and hers yours —hers and Alice's and Betty's and Carol's and Dorothy's and Evelyn's, all up the alphabet. Oh, I have seen you eye them, Sir, and they you, seen you draw close, seen them drawn to the image of Who You Are, Big Writer, Big Professor. If only you would wear your masks you might have them! But you make the mistake of wishing to be loved for yourself, not for your image, and that will never do, for you are all too true to yourself, who includes wife and children and writing machine.

No woman is going to go charging head foremost against such opposition. She will draw close, but then she will draw away. The way to win a woman is to promise her your undivided love, swear to her that you will divorce your wife, abandon your children, sell your typewriter, and marry her. You must stop being who you are. You must stop defining yourself because you do it all too frankly, all too well. You must not be you, but the accepted image of yourself, and then you will succeed with many women, because, you see, you are a most persuasive chap, and a good actor, so that you might easily play the role of romantic lover if only you didn't so deeply feel yourself solid citizen. These love affairs, so-called, may best be left to authors who, not having them, choose to invent them for innocent folk who don't have them either.

Then too, young man, select simpler women if it's bed and flesh you want. Be less ambitious. Want not Cecile nor Gabriella, for, while they are not so bright as I, they are bright enough to know what games not to play, what fights not to fight. Choose less experienced women. Choose, say, students, lassies of twenty, promise them you will renounce your family and sell your writing machine, and you will have with them a lovely life together for two or three days.

There is no charge for this counseling service, provided free to all our regular customers. All work done on premises.

I saw Paul on campus today. He said something about your Tenure Committee meeting, or not meeting. In the whirlwind company of Will Wood I couldn't quite hear.

Tetsey fine. Grandma Y writes happily of her house over-run, her garden stomped, wild horses tamed, and all Utah turned upside-down. (By Thanksgiving we simply must agree upon a firm, permanent policy with respect to the chiffonier.)

With all my love,

Friday, November 2

[to his wife, San Francisco]

DEPARTMENT OF POLICE
CHICAGO

November 2

Dear Beth,

I wouldn't be surprised if the postmark startled you, and the letterhead even more. It is comfy here. I am writing on the Chief's machine. He did not want to lend me his machine, but, glancing at the calendar on his wall, I reminded him that today is All Souls Day, and he could not resist. As I explained to him, I must write a little something every night, come rain or prison, as a cop must make his rounds. Last night, for the first time in a month, I wrote nobody, but all through October I wrote at least one useful letter every night, by way of keeping limber, solved many problems, relieved many difficulties, and clarified numerous obscurities.

You will be interested to know that yesterday—no, Wednesday—Whizzer Harlow and Gabriella Bodeen announced their intention to marry (each other). However, yesterday morning as I was leaving for Peekskill—yes, yesterday, Thursday—he wandered back into The Brown, a small hotel, and told me it was all off. On the train to Peekskill he fell in love with another, to whom hewas proposing marriage when she got off at Yonkers.

When we arrived at the camp Irwin was murdering a left-handed heavyweight named Zero Miranda, of Argentina. I reminded Garafolo that it is hardly a test of anything to feed left-handers to Irwin—that Irwin might as well punch the bag as slaughter a poor helpless immigrant. "Throw somebody in there," I said, "who'll hit him over the jab, otherwise Sanzobo is going to hit him there to the embarrassment of everyone on the 16th."

"Nobody's going to hurt him over the jab," Garafolo said.

"Yes they are," I said.

"No they won't," Garafolo said.

"Yes sir," said Whizzer. "Yes sir, somebody *will.*"

"Go home and goodby," Garafolo said. "I told you you were entirely welcome to come only not make a sound."

"Who is he," asked Whizzer, "to tell you you can't make a sound? Who does he think he is anyway, by God?"

"I could hit him over the jab," I said.

"Of course you could," said Whizzer.

"What that man want?" Irwin said.

"I know somebody who can knock you flat over your jab," I said.

"I refer all question to Mr. Gafo," Irwin said.

"I refer all questions to Mr. Garbage Pail," Garafolo said.

"How long can you stand this abuse?" Whizzer asked me.

"You know who can hit you over the jab?" I said to Irwin. "Me."

"Sure he can," Whizzer said.

"When?" said Irwin.

He is not any bigger than I am, nor, fundamentally, in any better condition. I was handsome in orange tights. My second was a Venezuelan bantam, Ike Calatayud. He tied me into gloves. Alexander Irwin's second was Garafolo. The audience was fighters and handlers and some newsmen and photographers, and Whizzer Harlow.

He came out of his corner slowly. I came out fast. He jabbed, and I hit him over the jab, a hard punch, and another, and his nose bled a trickle, and I hit him again, my right again, over his jab, and it occurred to me to reflect that I was demolishing my own investment, and my brother's, but I quickly told myself I was not demolishing it, but only instructing it, whereupon I hit him a fourth hard punch, and we swapped lefts, and his left stung. It is a good left. It is—they are—warm lefts. He was bleeding nicely from the nose, and I was closing his left eye with my right hand, trading hard rights for warm lefts—hot lefts—and I was taking them well. He, too, takes punishment well, for I punished him nicely with right hands to nose and eye before bethinking myself to glide leftward away from his jab, rest, then move back in again, and so I did, glided nicely, smoothly, good feet, glided free of his lefts, and he hit me with his right hand, and I was further defined. Garafolo sat me up with the salts to my nose, and he said, "Lee, every man to their own trade." The time of the bout was two minutes and thirty-five seconds.

I showered, I was medicated, I dressed, I ate at the table, and I went back into town with Whizzer. As we rode, I recalled a certain Ford automobile which had for some days been parked in front of the hotel, its key in the ignition, its windows open, its back seat loaded with books, and I was determined that if it still were there I should drive it to Chicago.

I don't know why I felt that that particular automobile belongs in Chicago. As for me, however, I belonged as much in Chicago as anywhere. Certainly I do not belong on Broadway, nor in the prize ring. Neither a Utah farm nor Harvard suits my taste. I am in sympathy with neither the beat generation nor The Dollar A Word Club. Tom Katt is dead, and Whizzer Harlow I have outgrown. I am the product of the process of elimination: my choice seems to be made for me. It is the reality. Why buck history? I keep telling the Chief I don't belong *here,* either. This place is full of citizens who this evening beat their wives or molested children or burgled, All Souls Day notwithstanding—"just simply not my kind of people," I tell the Chief, but he is cautious, as Chiefs are prone to be.

It was there. I packed my bags. I told Mr. Brown or Mr. Small that Mr. Enright would settle my bill, and I told Whizzer I was now about to steal an automobile.

"No," he said.

"Just watch," I said.

"It's like old times," he said.

"Stand guard," I said, "while I unpark it," and he stood on the sidewalk while I unparked, and I waved and happily drove away, and he chased me but he could not catch me, down the street and around the corner and over the Bridge and through the petroleum refineries of New Jersey and over the Turnpike and West past Elyria and through the dawn in Indiana. I drove at 90. (When I got out of town I picked it up a little.) And when I reached Chicago I stopped to phone the owner of the car, one Robert Joseph Andrew O'Burke, with whom the following dialogue ensued:

ME: Hello, O'Burke, my name is Lee Youngdahl.

O'BURKE: Hello, Lee, my name is Charles Dickens.

ME: Now listen here, Robert Joseph Andrew O'Burke, never mind the badinage because you're in serious trouble. Your car is stolen. Do you mind if I call you Robert Joseph Andrew for short?

O'BURKE: Where are you?

ME: Chicago.

O'BURKE: Goodby.

ME: Go and look and *see* if it's stolen.

O'BURKE: I know it's stolen. What do you think I am, a fool I don't know when my car is stolen? Bring it back. Who is this anyhow?

ME: My name is Lee Youngdahl. Don't be unreasonable because I can't bring it back. I'm in Chicago.

O'BURKE: Drive it back.

ME: I'm on my way to Utah.

O'BURKE: In my car?

ME: No, I'm flying.

O'BURKE: Goodby.

ME: Now wait a second, Robert Joseph, just wait a second. You're trying to think who I am. Right? You can't figure it out. I'm nobody you know. Right? It's not a gag now. Right?

O'BURKE: You could be in Chicago, but you couldn't be Lee Youngdahl.

ME: I *am* I tell you. I'm going to leave your car in a garage, all bills paid, and I'm going to send you the money so you can come and get it.

O'BURKE: Where were you born?

ME: Ogden, Utah.

O'BURKE: Tell me this. What's the name of the girl in *The Hard Puncher*?

ME: The one he has an affair with or the one he marries? Try to be a little more specific.

O'BURKE: OK, both.

ME: The one he marries is Betty, the one he had the affair with is Gloriana.

O'BURKE: Where?

ME: Marries or has the affair? Learn to pinpoint a question.

O'BURKE: Both.

ME: Marries in Utah, affair in Idaho.

O'BURKE: Jesus! What's the name of the dog in *The Utah Manner*?

ME: Good question. Lord Chesterfield.

O'BURKE (aside): You know, I think this might be Lee Youngdahl.

ME: It *is* Lee Youngdahl, and I stole your goddam automobile if you'll listen to me a minute, goddam it.

O'BURKE: Brother, if you're Lee Youngdahl it's an honor to have it stolen.

ME: Thank you, Robert, and I don't want you to worry about your car.

O'BURKE: Who's worried? *You're* apparently worried.

ME: I'm going to send you a check covering everything. I'll pay the garage, and I'll send you a note where it is.

O'BURKE: That'd be helpful.

ME: Never mind the sarcasm.

O'BURKE: Goodby, Sam.

ME: You don't believe me.

O'BURKE: No, I don't believe I do.

ME: Well, you'll see.

O'BURKE: Pardon me if I don't hang by my thumbs.

ME: Just wait. I'll wing it special.

O'BURKE: An honor if true. If you're you it's all right, but you're not. If you're who I think you are you're your usual stunning pain in the ass. You know who I think you are? I think you're Sam Fine.

ME: No. No. No. I'm Youngdahl.

O'BURKE: Like hell.

When I came out to the street a policeman was walking round and round the car. He was whistling softly. I remained concealed. He took the keys out of the ignition, examined them, and replaced them. He examined the books. He hefted my bags. He strolled whistling down the street, and whistling he turned the corner. But when I was seated behind the wheel he swiftly and mysteriously re-appeared, placed a restraining hand upon my elbow, and inquired, "Your car?"

"No," said I.

"Whose is it?"

"A friend's."

"You been in a fight?"

"Yes."

"With who?"

"With a colored man."

"What over?"

"A disagreement."

A pause.

"What's your occupation?" he asked.

"I'm a college professor."

"You're a college professor and you don't know it's against the law double-parking?"

"Sir," said I, "in California we frequently triple-park."

"What are you doing in Chicago?"

"I'm on my way to Utah."

"Driving?"

"Flying."

Another pause. He whistled a few bars. Then he asked, "Where's your friend you borrowed the car off?"

"He's in New York."

"How's he going to get his car?"

"He's coming out and get it."

"When?"

"As soon as I send him the money."

"I see." Once more, a pause. Once more, a strain of meditative music. Then he said, "I think you better come along with me," and he took me to his Chief, and my pockets were examined.

"You always carry so much cash with you?" asked the Chief. I have with me the $450 from Whizzer, and $1,000 in cash which Garafolo returned to me—the show-up guarantee.

"No."

"Where'd you get it?" the Chief asked.

"I won $450 in a bet, the rest a friend gave me."

"What kind of a friend? A colored friend?"

"No, a Corsican friend."

"The same friend that also loaned you the car?"

"No, I believe the friend who loaned me the car is an Irish friend."

The Chief said, "You *believe* . . ."

"Because you see," I said, "I've never met him."

"You never met him but he loaned you his car."

"Yes."

"You sure make friends quick," said the Chief. He and my arresting officer consulted briefly, and my interrogation was resumed. "What subject are you a professor of?"

"English."

"In San Francisco."

"Yes."

"Ain't school in session at the present moment?"

"Yes."

"Then why are you going to Utah?"

"My children are there, most of them, and my parents, my brother."

"How many children?"

"Seven. Six in Utah, one with my wife."

"You separated from your wife? Divorced?"

"No."

"Where is she?"

"She's living in San Francisco with a man from Ohio."

Is the man from Ohio a friend of yours?"

"Yes."

"Did you ever *meet* him?"

"No."

"What does your brother do?"

"He owns part of a prizefighter."

"A colored fighter?"

"Yes."

"Is he the one that beat you up?"

"Yes."

"With gloves on?"

"Yes."

"Why didn't you say so?"

"Because I want to see police action from the inside."

"Well now," said the Chief, "we'll show you a little police action from the inside. We'll show you how we check on your friend that loaned you the car, so you say. When we make a check like this do you know who pays the bill? *You* do. Ain't that an interesting detail of police action from the inside?"

Here is how he does it. He telephones the New York Police Department and requests that the New York Police Department visit Robert Joseph Andrew O'Burke for confirmation of my story. This is what the New York Police Department is currently doing. They are having little success, however, because Robert Joseph Andrew O'Burke has gone off somewhere with Sam Fine. They were expected home for supper, but they have not come. They were expected home *after* supper, but it is suspected that they have gone off to the theater. They were expected home after the theater, but it is likely, we are told, that they are entertaining certain young ladies whose names both the O'Burke residence and the Fine residence refuse to supply. It is midnight in New York, but they have not returned.

Get that man out of my daughter's bed!

With love,

Saturday, November 3

[special delivery]

IN THE AIR, CHICAGO TO OGDEN

November 3

Mr. Robert Joseph Andrew O'Burke
139 East 30th Street
New York, N. Y.

Dear Bob,

Herewith, I send you the following items: my personal check for $200; a storage ticket for your car, which is housed at Conroy's Park-It, 6012 South Green Street, Chicago. Ask for Jack.

When I arrive in San Francisco I shall send you autographed copies of my books. Stay home and read them, you dog, and don't be running around town all night. You have inconvenienced me no end. I replaced a tire in Columbus, where the man told me you strike him as the sort of fellow that doesn't think enough about flushing your radiator. Therefore I allowed your radiator to be flushed. If I can be of further service to you, do not hesitate to call upon me.

Yours truly,

[*enclosures to O'Burke: personal check, Bank of America, $200; automobile storage ticket, Conroy's Park-It, 6012 South Green Street, Chicago 21.*]

Sunday, November 4

[to Harold Rosenblatt, New Haven, Conn.]

November 4

Dear Harold,

Once before—about fifteen years ago—I came home from the east to Ogden to meditate upon my triumphant wounds, and here I am again. Your cynicism notwithstanding, the purpose of my trip was plentifully clear to me, my business was accomplished with unforeseen rapidity, I routed myself back through Chicago, and I write you now to ask your permission to request of your rentors that they admit a friend of mine to your spare bedroom for a few days next month. He is a Broadway producer, and, while he is far from impecunious, the expense of lying down in the Mark Hopkins is a trifle awkward.

Did you receive the box of oat-cakes I sent you? I discovered the shop while strolling one night with a theater associate. Dashing within, I told its proprietors, a Mr. and Mrs. Dunnichen, "I must taste an oat-cake."

"Oh Sir," said Mrs. Dunnichen, "we haven't made oat-cakes in years. The tradition, Sir, has died with the passing of the New-York Scotch."

"But we can make an oat-cake yet," said her husband.

"Make me one," I said.

"Oh Sir," said she, "we couldn't make *one*."

"Make me three boxes then," said I, "a box for my wife, a box for me, and a box for Harold."

She assured me that her oat-cakes were genuine, prepared in the manner her mother had taught her, who in turn was taught by her mother before her, backward in time to the generation of the mother of the mother of James Boswell. "When we first set up to make oat-cakes here," she said, "they were in demand."

"But then, Sir," said her husband, "to suit the changing taste we took to making English muffins."

"Or what they call hereabouts English muffins," said his wife.

"For they aren't rightly English," he said.

"Nor rightly muffins neither," said Mrs. Dunnichen.

"It is this city," I said. "It is a whoredom."

"Not at all," said Mr. Dunnichen. "There's whores in every city, in every age, and now no different."

"Somebody somewhere," said Mrs. Dunnichen, "will always be keeping high the tradition of oat-cakes."

"Somewhere," said her husband, "somebody will always go on calling things by their right name."

So speak to me no more of dreams of eastern glory. Tempt me no more to match your eastern honors with honors of my own. Make me not jealous. Hereafter, when you are invited somewhere, I shall not envy you. I shall remain at home by my window, looking out on yours.

My Tenure Committee has met. They fought furiously. They debated, wrangled, smoked cigarettes, adjourned to caucus, lobbied, orated, made deals, cast ballot after ballot for a minute or more, and then they unanimously voted me In. I said to Beth, "You know, sometimes my imagination tends to drift ahead of the facts. Sometimes I almost think my mind betrays a slight inclination to create conflict where none exists."

"Of course it does," she said, "that's what makes you a writer, darling . . ."

[*the end*]

A NOTE ON THE AUTHOR

Mark Harris was born in 1922 in Mt. Vernon, N. Y. He now teaches English at San Francisco State College, where he lives with his wife and two children, and where, he says, he sneaks off daily to his writing. Before that he was a student, a newspaperman, and a soldier.

He wrote his first novel, *Trumpet to the World* (1946), in South Carolina and Georgia; his biography of Vachel Lindsay, *City of Discontent* (1952), in Illinois and New Mexico; his second novel, which was also his first novel in the Henry Wiggen manner, *The Southpaw* (1953), in Colorado; his third, *Bang the Drum Slowly* (1956), and his fourth, *A Ticket for a Seamstitch* (1957), in California. Another novel, *Something About a Soldier,* was published in 1957. After the Henry Wiggen novels appeared, critics began to hail him as a major American writer.

In 1953 he was a resident at the MacDowell Colony in Peterborough, N. H., and in 1957–8 he spent an exciting academic year as an exchange professor in Japan.

A NOTE ON THE TYPE

The text of this book was set on the Linotype in a face called Baskerville, named for John Baskerville (1706–75), of Birmingham, England, who was a writing master with a special renown for cutting inscriptions in stone. About 1750 he began experimenting with punch-cutting and making typographical material, which led, in 1757, to the publication of his first work, a Virgil in royal quarto, with great primer letters, in which the types throughout had been designed by him. This was followed by his famous editions of Milton, the Bible, the Book of Common Prayer, and several Latin classic authors. His types foreshadowed what we know today as the "modern" group of type faces, and these and his printing became greatly admired. After his death Baskerville's widow sold all his punches and matrices to the SOCIÉTÉ PHILOSOPHIQUE, LITTÉRAIRE ET TYPOGRAPHIQUE (totally embodied in the person of Beaumarchais, author of THE MARRIAGE OF FIGARO and THE BARBER OF SEVILLE), which used some of the types to print the seventy-volume edition, at Kehl, of Voltaire's works. After a checkered career on the Continent, where they dropped out of sight for some years, the punches and matrices finally came into the possession of the distinguished Paris type-founders Deberny & Peignot, who, in singularly generous fashion, returned them to the Cambridge University Press in 1953.

Composed, printed, and bound by THE COLONIAL PRESS INC., Clinton, Massachusetts. Paper manufactured by S. D. WARREN COMPANY, Boston. Cover design by PAUL RAND. Typography by HARRY FORD.